More Praise for

Home After Dark

"An important novel about adolescence and the search for identity. . . . Small is a masterful illustrator, with an incredible ability to establish his characters' inner lives through physical gestures or facial expressions, conveying a kaleidoscopic style of storytelling reminiscent of filmmaker Terrence Malick. . . . [A] resonant and stirring work."

– *Library Journal* (starred review)

"[A] haunting coming-of-age tale. . . . In a hero's-journey narrative punctuated by episodic adventures, Russell searches for a sense of 'home,' as Small again juxtaposes the horrors of an unhappy childhood with the bleak underbelly of 1950s and '60s America illustrated with his signature fine pen lines and grey wash."

– *Publishers Weekly* (starred review)

"Evocative and heartbreaking and simple and pure. . . . Think of *Lord of the Flies* and *The Catcher in the Rye* joined as one, yet even more painfully honest. This is a haunting work of unfolding surprise. Few words, cinematic pictures, dazzling art."

– Jules Feiffer, author of the *Kill My Mother* Trilogy

"David Small's extraordinary new graphic novel, *Home After Dark*, is the story of Russell, a teenaged boy abandoned first by his mother and then by his father. It's about Russell's adolescence but also everyone's: learning who you can and can't trust, the complexities of relationships with your peers, and figuring out who you are and the kind of person you want to be. Russell's struggle to survive and not be crushed by the indifference or cruelty of the world drew me in. The drawings are gorgeous and expressive – Small's facial expressions alone filled me with awe. A wonderful book and a great follow-up to *Stitches*."

– Roz Chast, cartoonist for *The New Yorker*

"[David Small is] a master graphic storyteller who has certainly captured male adolescence in 1950s America. Having to think about dodging high school bullies every day sure resonated with me! And Russell's sexual predicament was handled in a very original way."

– Robert Crumb, author of *The Book of Genesis Illustrated by R. Crumb*

"The silence of David Small's masterful drawings has put words in my mouth – words that recapture the inchoate chaos of youth."

– Jack Gantos, winner of the Newbery Award and author of *Hole in My Life*

HOME AFTER DARK

A NOVEL

DAVID SMALL

McClelland & Stewart

Library and Archives Canada Cataloguing in Publication

Small, David, 1945-, author, illustrator
Home after dark / David Small.
Issued also in print and electronic formats.
ISBN 978-0-7710-7932-0 (hardcover).--ISBN 978-0-7710-7934-4 (EPUB)
1. Graphic novels. I. Title.
PN6727.S44H66 2018 741.5'973 C2018-900560-2
C2018-900561-0

Published simultaneously in the United States of America by Liveright Publishing Corporation, a division of W. W. Norton & Company, Inc., 500 Fifth Avenue, New York, NY 10110.

Home After Dark is a work of fiction. Names, characters, places, and incidents are the products of the author's imagination or are used fictitiously. Any resemblance to actual events, locales, or persons, living or dead, is entirely coincidental.

Printed and bound in the USA

McClelland & Stewart,
a division of Penguin Random House Canada Limited,
a Penguin Random House Company
www.penguinrandomhouse.ca

1 2 3 4 5 22 21 20 19 18

TO MIKE KLEIMO, KEVIN BRADY, MARK GUIN, AND BRAD ZELLAR
FOR THEIR MEMORIES,
AND, AS EVER,
TO MY WIFE, SARAH,
FOR HER LOVE, HER PATIENCE, AND HER ENDURANCE.

HOME AFTER DARK

PROLOGUE
YOUNGSTOWN, OHIO

KRASH!

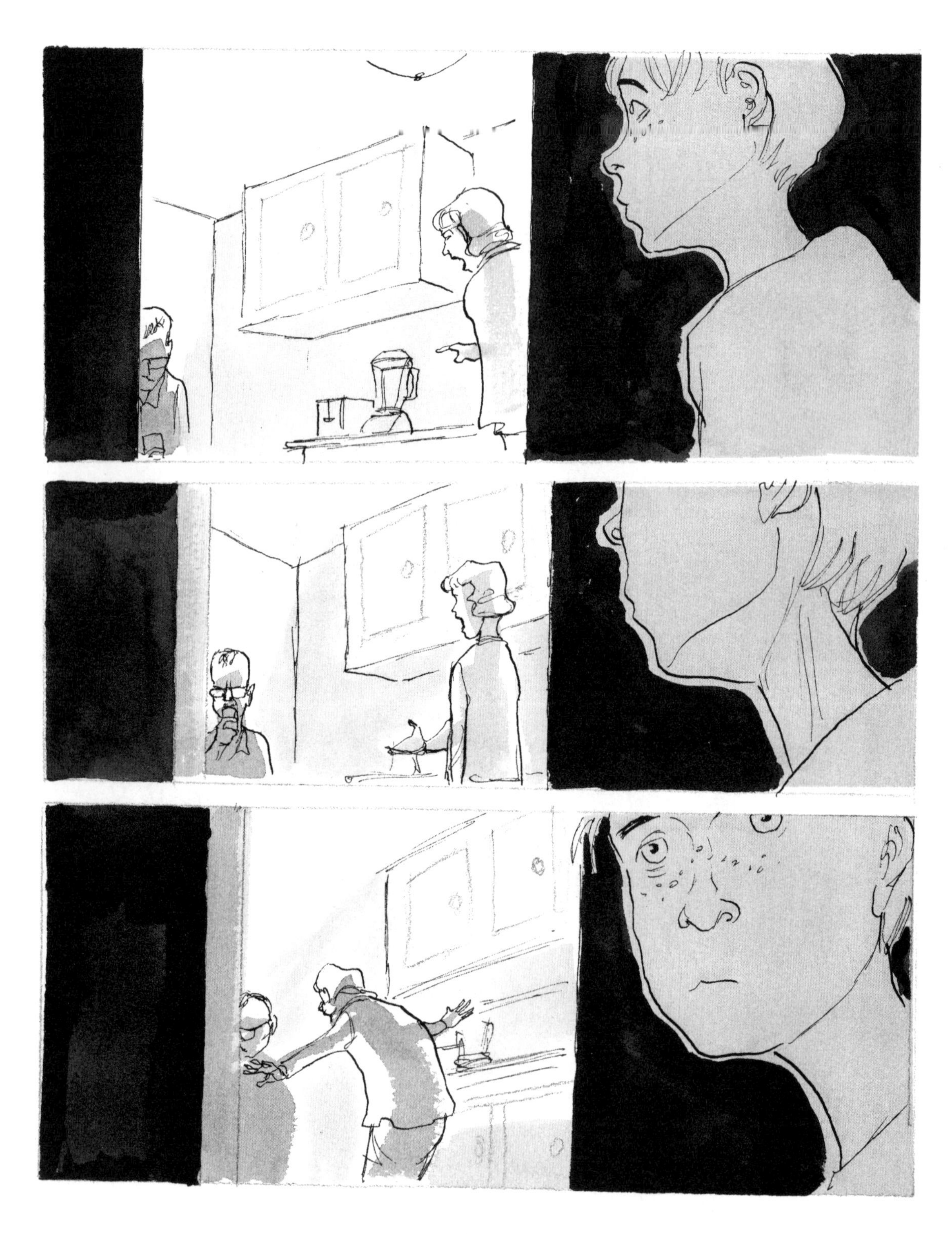

THAT NIGHT, WHEN THE SCREAMING AND SHOUTING BEGAN, IT WAS LIKE HEARING MY PARENTS' REAL VOICES FOR THE FIRST TIME.

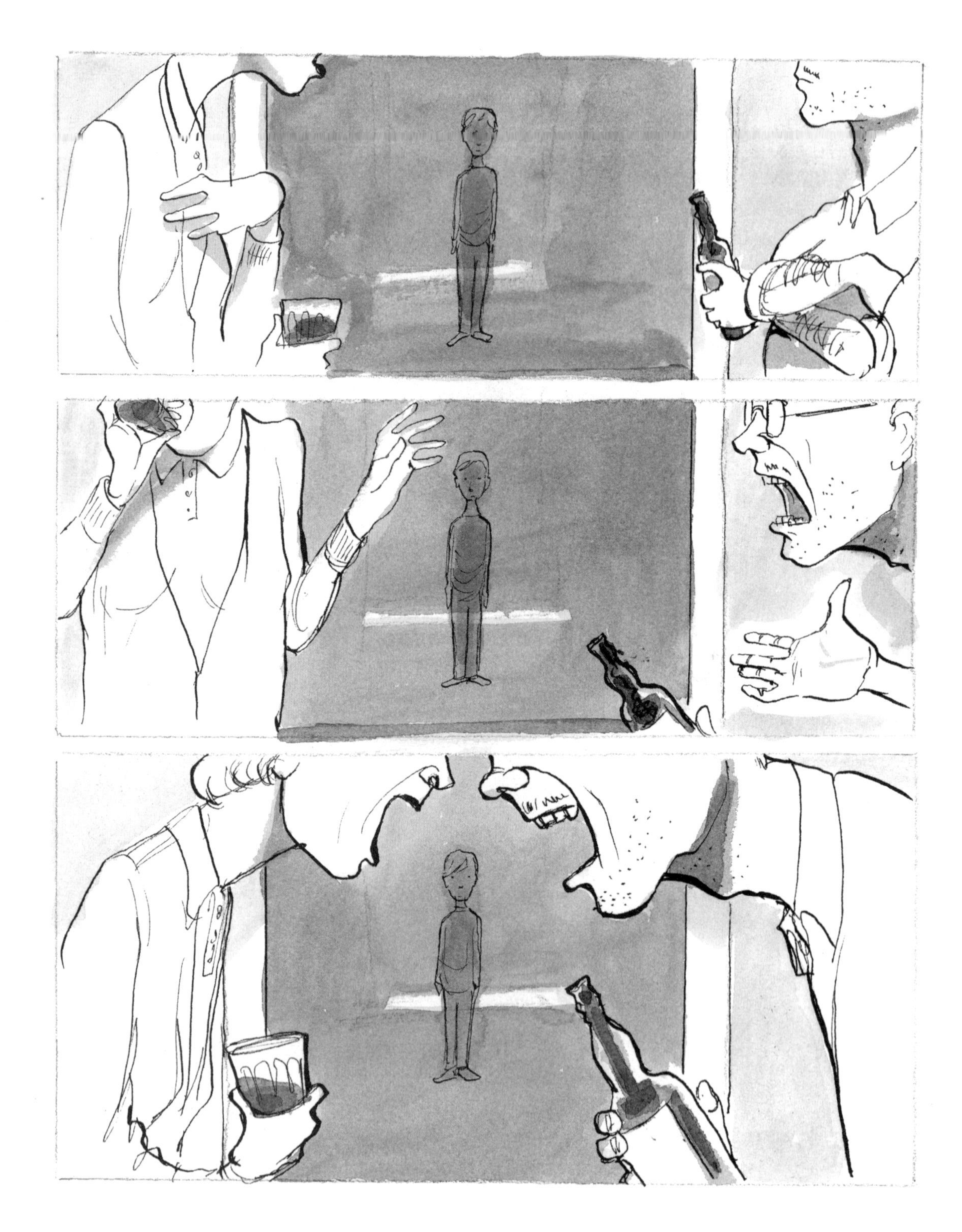

THAT SUMMER, MOM RAN AWAY WITH OLLIE JACKSON (KNOWN ON THE FOOTBALL FIELD AS "ACTION JACKSON"), DAD'S BEST FRIEND.

DAD DECIDED TO MOVE US TO CALIFORNIA.

AFTER HIS STINT IN THE KOREAN WAR, THEN THE DIVORCE, I GUESS ALL HE COULD THINK OF WAS THAT DREAM OF SUN, SAND, AND GOLDEN BODIES.

CHAPTER ONE
SOLD

HE HAD AN OLDER SISTER IN PASADENA. MY AUNT JUNE, WHOM I HAD NEVER MET.

WE WOULD LIVE WITH HER UNTIL HE FOUND A JOB, HE TOLD ME. IT WAS ALL ARRANGED, HE SAID.

CALIFORNIA

GREETINGS from
PASADENA
CALIFORNIA

KUT RATE
MOTEL
VACANCY
OFFICE

HEY, DAD? THERE'S A PUPPY!

THE ANSWER IS "NO."

BUT HE MIGHT STARVE!

DON'T TOUCH IT! IT PROBABLY HAS RABIES.

MAYBE YOU CAN HAVE A DOG WHEN WE GET TO CALIFORNIA.

TOOOT
FLAMMABLE

CHAPTER TWO

PASADENA,
CALIFORNIA
Stan's
BOWL
BAR
OHIO

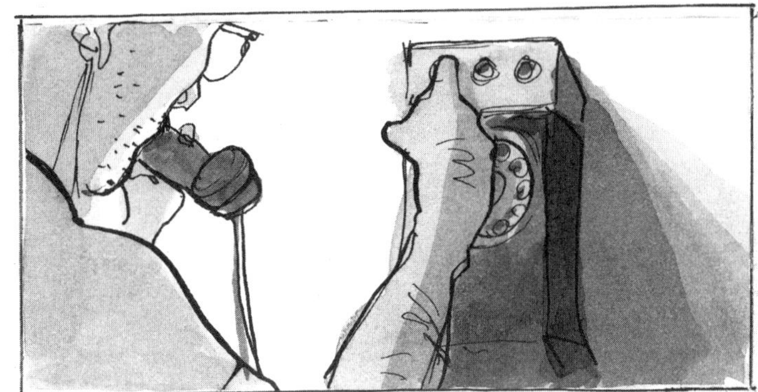

TELEPHONE
HI, JUNE. IT'S ME.
WE JUST GOT IN.
IS IT TOO LATE TO COME OVER?

THAT'S RIGHT. "WE." RUSSELL IS WITH ME. MY SON? YOUR NEPHEW?

I TOLD YOU I WAS BRINGING HIM WITH ME.

HOW OLD IS HE?

RUSSELL! HOW OLD ARE YOU?
I'M THIRTEEN.

HE'S THIRTEEN.
OK. FINE! WE'LL DISCUSS IT TOMORROW.

MOTEL
VACANCY

HOLY CRAP! IS THIS WHERE WE'RE GOING TO LIVE?

WATCH YOUR MOUTH. YOU CAN'T SAY THINGS LIKE "HOLY CRAP" AROUND AUNT JUNE.

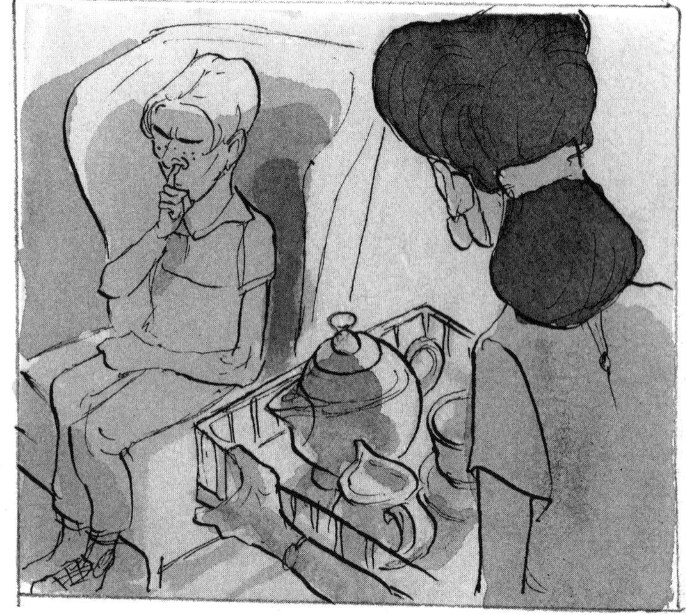

DON'T YOU HAVE A HANDKERCHIEF, YOUNG MAN?

JUNE, MY COMPENSATION HAS NEARLY RUN OUT. BUT I'LL START LOOKING FOR WORK RIGHT AWAY.

WHEN I GET A JOB I CAN GET A LOAN ON THE G.I. BILL AND GET A HOUSE.
WE'LL BE OUT OF YOUR HAIR IN NO TIME.

MIKE . . .
YOU WON'T BE IN MY HAIR.
YOU WON'T BE STAYING HERE.
THIS IS SOUTHERN CALIFORNIA. REAL ESTATE IS GOING NUTS. MIKE, LET'S FACE IT, YOU CAN'T AFFORD TO LIVE HERE. YOU NEED TO GO NORTH, AROUND SAN FRANCISCO. THAT'S WHERE ALL THE JOBS ARE.

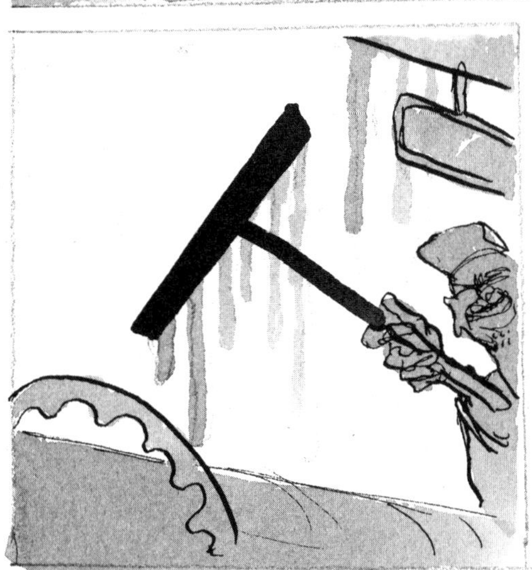

GAS

CHAPTER THREE

AUNT JUNE WAS WRONG. JOBS WERE NOT TO BE FOUND NEAR SAN FRANCISCO. WE KEPT GOING NORTH AND FARTHER INLAND, TO A LITTLE TOWN CALLED MARSHFIELD.

CHRIST! THIS COULD BE "ANYWHERE U.S.A."!

Welcome to
MARSHF
CALIFORNI

LIONS
L
INTERNATIONAL
G

DAD. THEY HAVE SOMETHING CALLED THE LIONS CLUB. WHAT'S THAT?
A GROUP.
VERY EXCLUSIVE. HARD TO GET IN.

"FOR MEN ONLY."

LET'S SEE WHAT'S FOR RENT AROUND HERE.

ANIMAL SLAYINGS CONTINUE IN MARSHFIELD
NO SUSPECTS FOUND

THE INDEPEND
ANIMAL SLAYINGS CONTINUE in MARSHFIELD
DAD, DID YOU SEE THIS?
YEH?
THAT'S SMALL TOWN "BIG NEWS." PEOPLE HAVEN'T GOT ENOUGH TO DO. THEY GET ALL EXCITED OVER A DEAD COW.
BUT IT SAYS THERE HAVE BEEN A LOT OF ANIMALS MURDERED . . .
BIG DEAL.

FOR A TIME WE RENTED A ROOM FROM THE MAHS, WHO OWNED A RESTAURANT IN LITTLE CHINA HARBOR, DOWN BY THE BAY.
ROOM TO LET

PLEASE COME IN.
I'LL SHOW YOU THE ROOM.

MY NAME IS WEN AND THIS IS MY HUSBAND JIAN.
JIAN SPEAKS NO ENGLISH, BUT HE UNDERSTANDS EVERYTHING YOU SAY.
THE ROOM IS THIS WAY.

YOU WILL HAVE ONE BEDROOM WITH TWO BEDS. YOUR BATH IS ACROSS THE HALL.
YOU MAY ALSO USE THE KITCHEN AND PATIO.

OR MAYBE YOU WOULD PREFER I COOK FOR YOU?
FOR A LITTLE EXTRA?

YES! I'D VERY MUCH PREFER YOU COOK FOR US!

THIS HOUSE SMELLS FUNNY.
THAT'S CHINESE COOKING.
I'M OFF TO SHOWER.

CALIFORNIA.
WOULD I
EVER GET
USED TO IT?

MORNINGS, WHILE DAD WAS LOOKING FOR WORK AND THE MAHS WERE AT THEIR RESTAURANT, ALONE, I SCOPED OUT THE HOUSE.

HEY, KID!
WAIT UP!

YOU AND YOUR OLD MAN RENT ROOMS UP THE STREET?

YES, SIR. FROM THE MAHS.

WELL, YOU TELL THOSE JAPS THEY AREN'T WANTED HERE.

THEY AREN'T JAPS. THEY'RE CHINESE.

BIG DIFFERENCE!

TELL THOSE CHINKS TO GET BACK TO THE LAUNDRY, WHERE THEY BELONG.

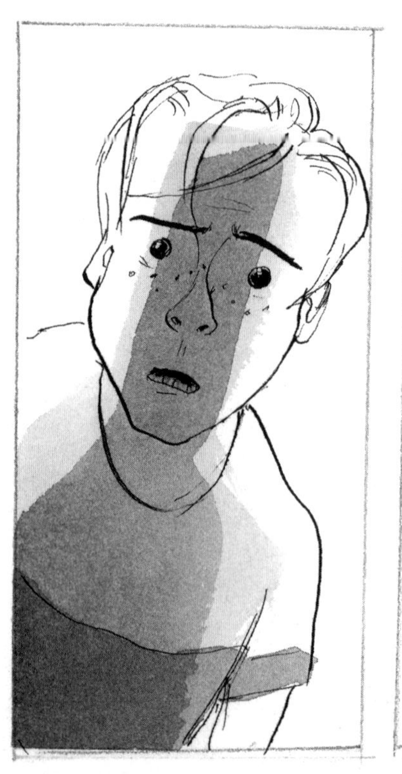

CATS?
KITTENS. THEIR HEADS WERE SHOVED THROUGH A FENCE.
PROBABLY JUST SOME KIDS MESS-ING AROUND.

RUSSELL!
FOR GOD'S SAKE STOP BEING SUCH A WIMP!

I HAVE AN ANNOUNCEMENT TO MAKE.

TODAY I GOT A JOB.

MIKE! CONGRATULATIONS! WHAT'S THE JOB?

WELL, IT'S NOT EXACTLY WHAT I WAS LOOKING FOR.

I'LL BE TEACHING ENGLISH.
AT SAN QUENTIN.

THE PRISON?

THAT'S SO INTER-ESTING.

YOU WILL BE TEACHING SHAKESPEARE TO THE INMATES?

NO. I'LL BE TEACHING THEM TO SAY, "THERE IS THE DOOR." "THIS IS A BROWN DOG." THAT SORT OF ENGLISH.

THAT'S GOOD! MAYBE YOU CAN TEACH JIAN SOME OF THAT.
HE NEEDS IT!

WE HAVE TO CELEBRATE!

CHAPTER FOUR

WITH A LOAN FROM THE G.I. BILL DAD WAS ABLE TO BUY ONE OF THE NEW LITTLE HOUSES SPRINGING UP LIKE TOADSTOOLS IN MARSHFIELD.

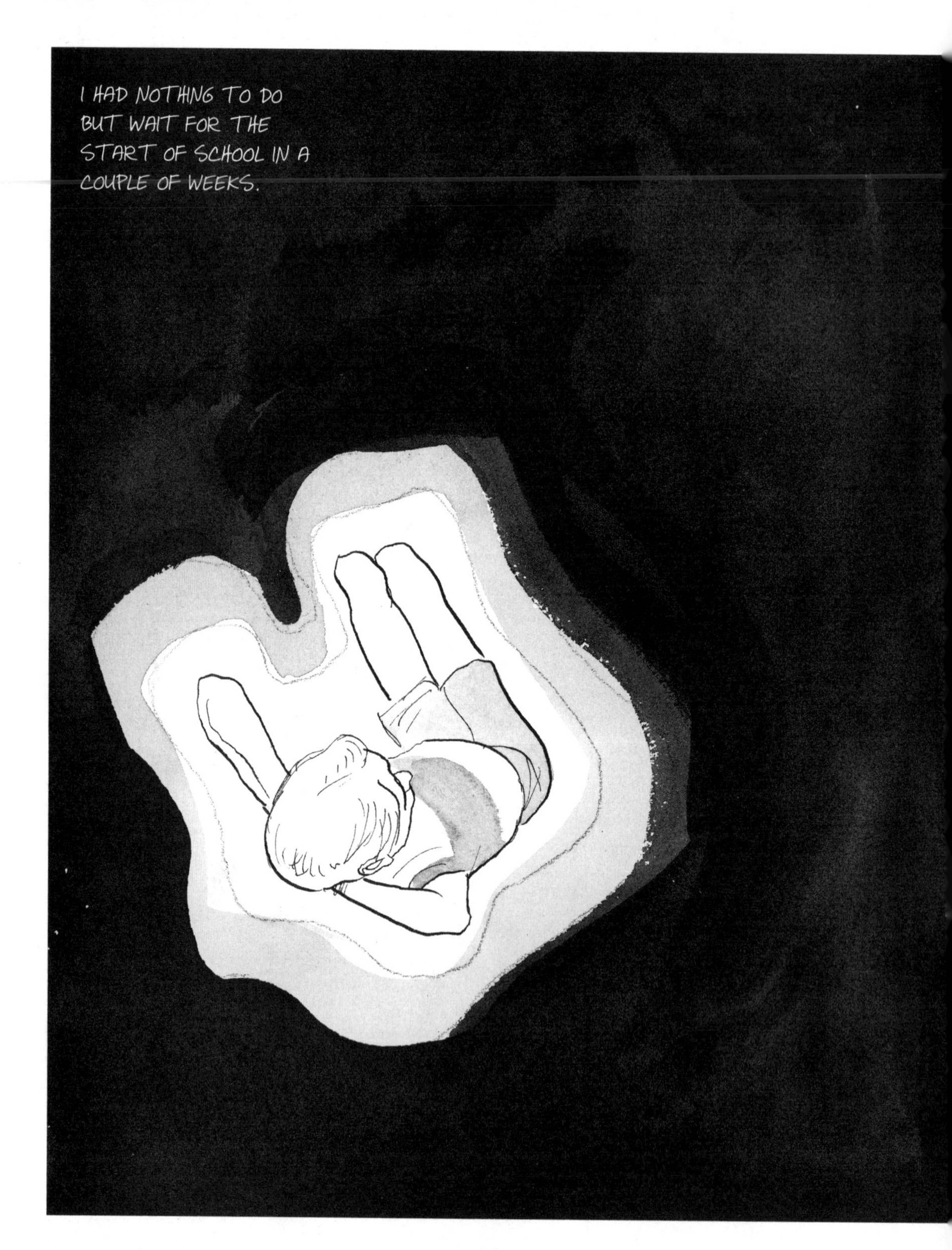
I HAD NOTHING TO DO BUT WAIT FOR THE START OF SCHOOL IN A COUPLE OF WEEKS.

DAD CONTINUED PAYING MRS. MAH TO BRING US OUR EVENING MEALS.

I TRIED TO HAVE SUPPER WARMING BY THE TIME DAD ARRIVED HOME.
SLAM!

CRUSH!
DAD! ARE YOU ALL RIGHT?
FUCK.

GO INSIDE.
KLIK!
Fwoosh!

KLIK

HERE'S ANOTHER OF MRS. MAH'S CONCOCTIONS.
HOPE YOU LIKE IT!

"HOPE YOU LIKE IT"!
GODDAMNIT, RUSSELL, I CAN WARM UP MY OWN SUPPER.
THE LAST THING I NEED IS MY SON BECOMING A HAUSFRAU.

THAT NIGHT I DREAMED . . .
I HAD A JOB AT THE LIONS CLUB ("FOR MEN ONLY").

SAY, MIKE, ISN'T THAT YOUR SON?

THAT REMAINS TO BE SEEN.

ONE,
TWO . . .
HEAVE . . .
HO!

CHAPTER FIVE

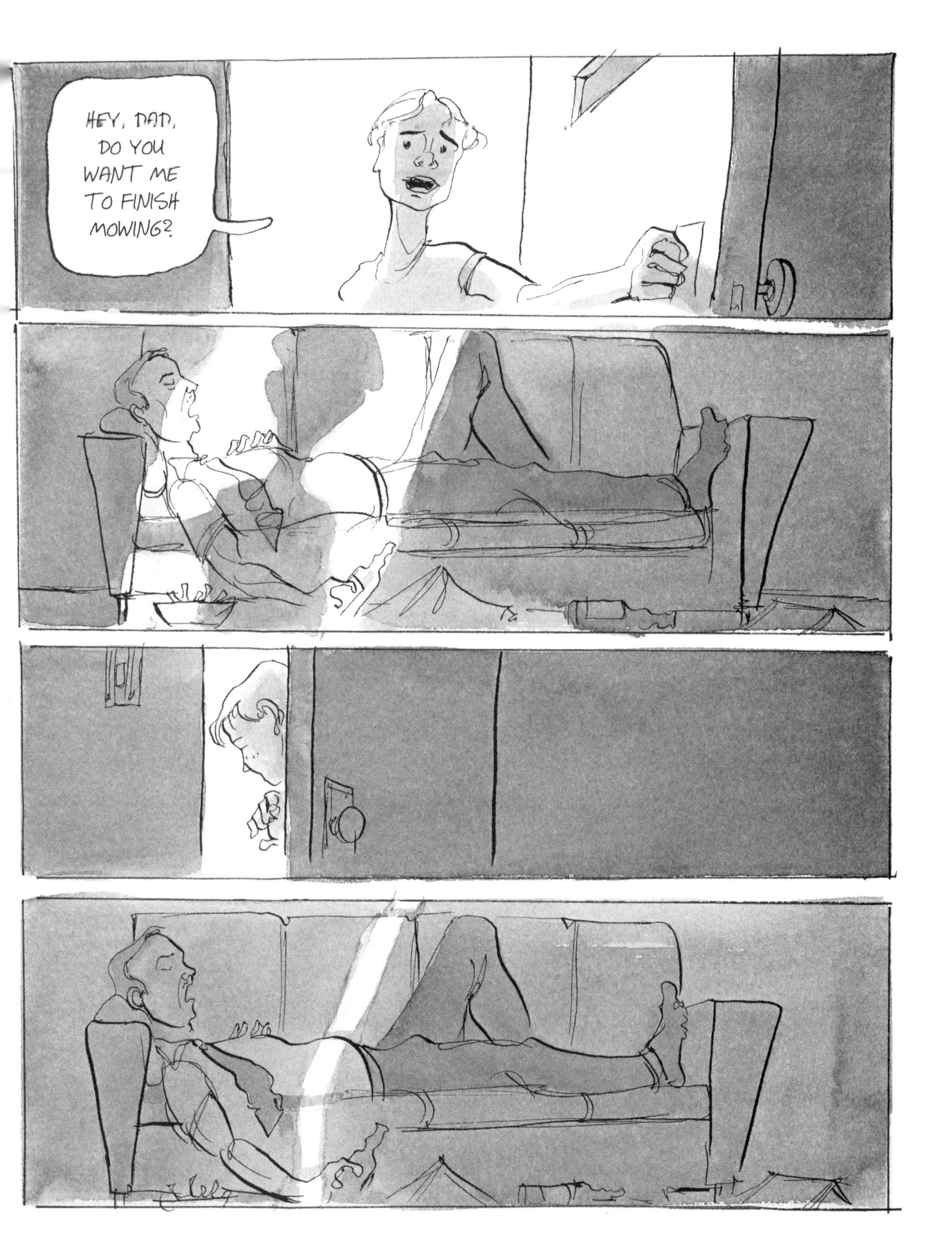
HEY, DAD, DO YOU WANT ME TO FINISH MOWING?

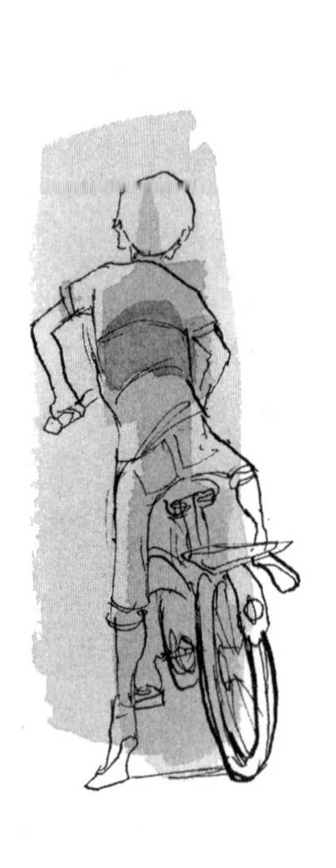

HEY, KID!
WAIT UP!

DON'T RUN AWAY!

I'M WILLIE.
WE LIVE JUST DOWN THE BLOCK.

I'M KURT.
I'M RUSSELL.

WE WATCHED YOU MOVE IN.

HEY! WE ALL HAVE SCHWINNS!

WE'RE GOING TO THE ARROYO. WANNA COME?
WHAT'S THAT?
YOU GOTTA SEE THE ARROYO!

HEY, RUSS,
WHAT'S WITH THE
STRIPED SHIRT?
YEAH, MAN,
WHAT'S
THAT ALL
ABOUT?
WHAT'S
WRONG
WITH MY
SHIRT?
WHY DON'T YOU JUST
CARVE THE WORD
"DORK" INTO YOUR
FOREHEAD AND BE
DONE WITH
IT?
YOU GOTTA
GET YOURSELF
SOME WHITE
TEES, MAN!

HERE IT IS!
PARADISE!

COME ON DOWN, RUSS!

SO, WHAT DO YOU THINK?
INTERESTING.

ISN'T IT GREAT?
THIS IS OUR TERRITORY!

ARE YOU AFRAID?

OF COURSE NOT.
FIRST DAY OF SCHOOL'S TOMORROW.
PAIN. AGONY. SUFFERING.
BOREDOM.
CAFETERIA FOOD.

WHAT GRADE ARE YOU IN?
I'M IN SEVENTH. KURT'S IN EIGHTH.

DO YOU GUYS BIKE TO SCHOOL? MAYBE WE COULD ALL GO TOGETHER.

THAT WOULD BE COOL, BUT YOU GO TO PUBLIC SCHOOL, RIGHT?
WE GO TO "OUR LADY."

SEE YA, RUSS.
ADIOS, RUSS.

CHAPTER SIX

HEY, KID!

IS THAT A SCHWINN "PANTHER"?
YES.

COME HERE A MINUTE.
I WANNA ASK YOU SOMETHING.

OOPS!

THE SPAZ! HE TRIPPED!
HA HA HA.
TELL ME, ARE THOSE LEVI'S YOU'RE WEARING?
YES.
UH-OH!
I'M GUNNA SHOW YOU WHAT WE DO TO **LITTLE FAGS** WHO DARE TO WEAR **REAL** MEN'S PANTS . . .

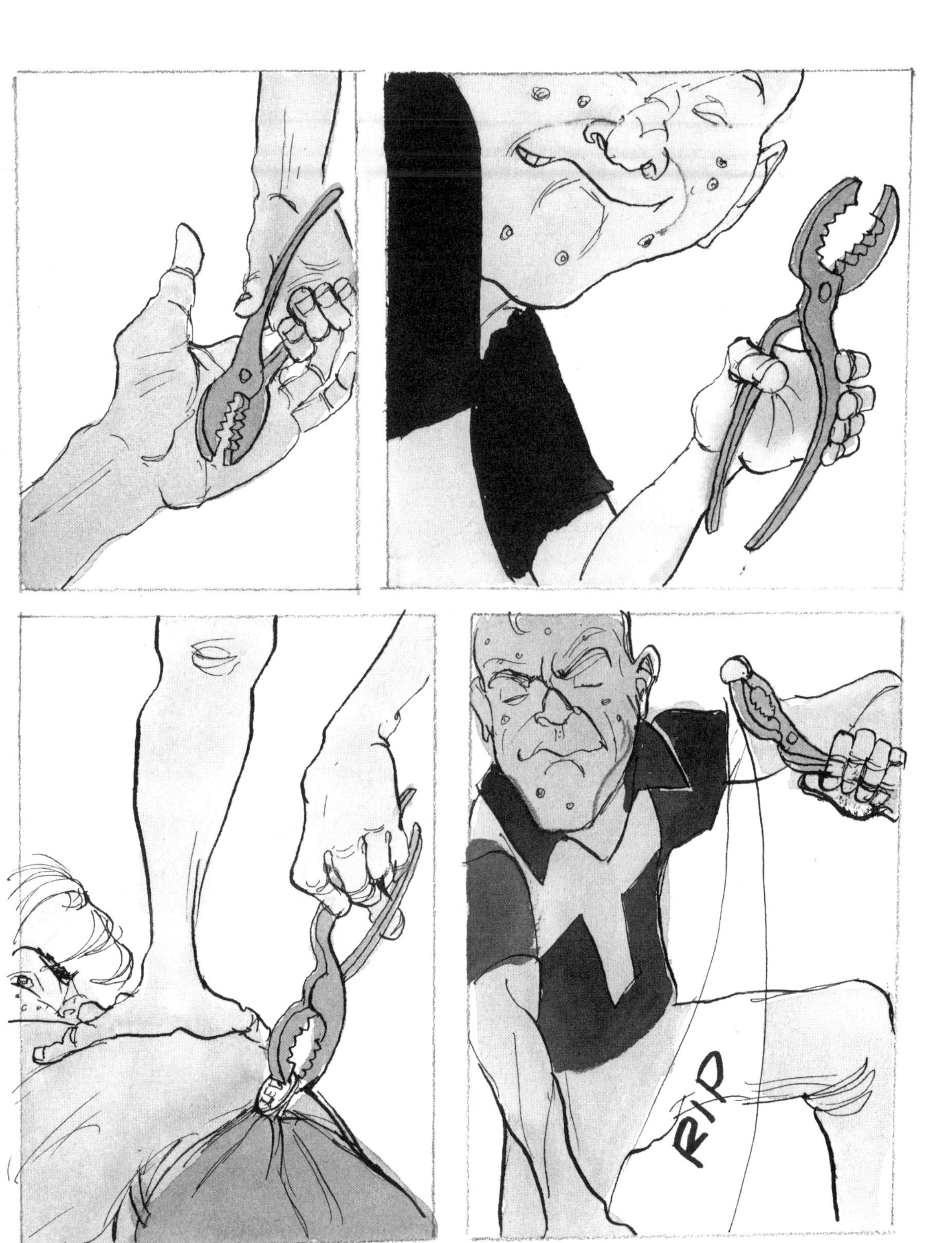
RIP

MIDDLE SCHOOL

RUSSELL PRUITT? YOU'RE LATE, RUSSELL. TAKE A SEAT IN THE BACK ROW.

DID THOSE BASTARDS RIP THE BUTTON OFF YOUR JEANS?
THEY DID THAT TO ME.
ONCE.
NEVER AGAIN.

WHAT DID YOU DO, REPORT THEM?
AND GET MY ASS KICKED? HELL NO.
I BECAME INVISIBLE.

MEET ME IN THE HALL AFTER SCHOOL AND I'LL SHOW YOU MY SECRET.

ONWARD!

SEE? DAYLIGHT!

IT'S THE JANITOR'S ENTRANCE. HE ALWAYS LEAVES THE DOOR OPEN SO HE CAN COME OUT FOR A SMOKE EVERY FIFTEEN MINUTES OR SO!

HIS NAME WAS WARREN McCAW.
WE CAN MEET HERE EVERY MORNING, IF YOU WANT.
SURE. WHY NOT?

CHAPTER SEVEN

BLAM

YOU'RE A PRETTY FAIR SHOT!

YOU KIDDING?
I'M A DAMN **GOOD** SHOT!

WHERE'D YOU GET THE GUN?
MY DAD.

HE LETS YOU TAKE IT?
NO . . .

HE LEFT US WHEN I WAS BORN. HE LEFT HIS GUN BEHIND, TOO.

KRAK

OFF WITH HIS HEAD!

WHAT ABOUT YOUR MOM?
SHE DOESN'T CARE IF YOU SHOOT?

MY MOM DIED.
I LIVE WITH MY GRANDMA NOW. SHE TAUGHT ME HOW TO SHOOT.
IS THERE GOOD HUNTING AROUND HERE?

I WOULDN'T KNOW.
IT'S JUST THE TARGET PRACTICE I LIKE.

WANT TO TRY IT?
NEXT TIME, MAYBE.

LET'S GO TO TOWN AND GET SOME COKES. I'M PARCHED.

LOOK! THERE'S THE PACIFIC OCEAN!
I KNOW SOME PEOPLE IN THIS BACKWATER WHO'VE NEVER EVEN BEEN TO SEE IT! CAN YOU BELIEVE THAT?

AND LOOK,

WAY DOWN THERE IS THE "Q." SAN QUENTIN.

MY DAD WORKS THERE.

AS A GUARD?

NO. HE TEACHES ENGLISH.

YOU MEAN HE TEACHES SHAKESPEARE TO CRIMINALS?
SOMETHING LIKE THAT.

7up

TWO COKES,
TEN CENTS.

YOU GO AHEAD,
I DON'T NEED
ONE.

NOT THIRSTY?
ACTUALLY, I DON'T HAVE ANY MONEY.
TEN CENTS.
WHEN YOU'RE WITH ME, RUSS, YOU DON'T HAVE TO WORRY ABOUT MONEY.

TODAY I BROUGHT SOMETHING SPECIAL TO SHOW YOU.

WHERE'D YOU GO?

THERE HE IS!

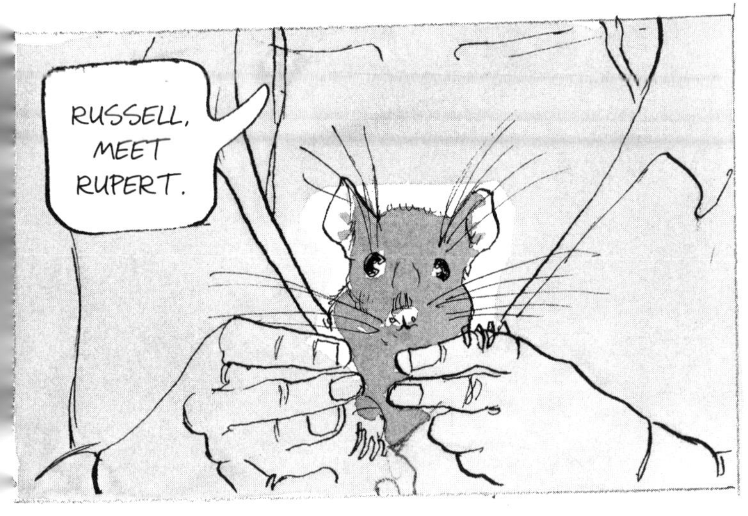
RUSSELL, MEET RUPERT.

GOD! WHAT IS THAT? A RAT?
YEP.
MY PET RAT!

HOW CAN YOU CARRY IT AROUND IN YOUR SHIRT? DOESN'T IT BITE?
NOPE. NEVER.

RATS ARE VERY MISUNDERSTOOD LITTLE CREA-TURES. THEY'RE ACTUALLY REALLY SMART.
AND CLEAN!

AND CUDDLY, TOO!
WANT TO PET HIM?

NAH. THANKS.

POOR RUPERT!
WHAT'S THAT AROUND YOUR NECK?
THESE?
THEY'RE CALLED AMULETS. THEY'RE LIKE MAGIC CHARMS.
MY GRANDMA GAVE THEM TO ME. TO PROTECT ME FROM EVIL, SHE SAID.
GRANNY'S A BIT SUPERSTITIOUS.
I WEAR THEM TO MAKE HER HAPPY.

I MUST ADMIT, IT DID MAKE ME WONDER IF I SHOULD RISK BEING SEEN WITH A KID WHO WORE TRINKETS AND CARRIED AROUND A RAT IN HIS SHIRT.

BUT THAT DIDN'T LAST, BECAUSE WARREN'S MONEY KEPT FLOWING.
HERSHEY'S
HERSHEY'S
SNICKERS

TOMORROW, WHY DON'T YOU COME OVER TO MY HOUSE?

OKAY. SURE.

CHAPTER EIGHT

ARK
ARK
ARK
ARK
ARK

ROWF!
ROWF!
ROWF!

THERE ARE SO MANY GUARD DOGS HERE . . .

YIP YIP YIP
YIP YIP
YOU'D THINK IT WAS FORT KNOX!

ARK
ARK
ARK

DON'T WORRY. IT'S REALLY PRETTY PEACEFUL AROUND HERE.

MOST OF THESE FOLKS WORK THIRD SHIFT, SO THEY SLEEP ALL DAY, LIKE VAMPIRES.

OUR PLACE IS AT THE END OF THE LANE.

OH, LOOK! THERE'S GRANNY!
YOU'LL GET TO MEET HER! GOOD!

GRANNY! HI!

OH, DEAR! I'M GOING TO BE LATE FOR BINGO!

I'LL HAVE SUPPER READY WHEN YOU GET HOME.
SWEET BOY!

WAIT! LET ME GIVE YOU SOME MONEY . . .

GRANNY, I DON'T NEED ANY.
TAKE IT! YOU NEVER KNOW.
YOUR GRANDMA IS REALLY GENEROUS WITH YOU.
SHE'S CRAZY-GENEROUS! BUT I DO HELP HER OUT A LOT, WITH CHORES.

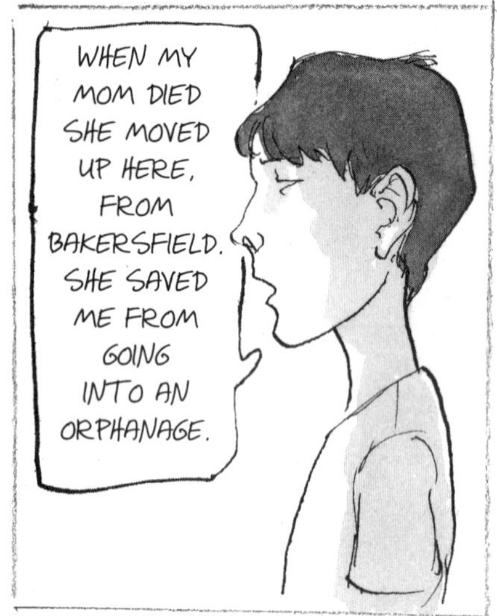
WHEN MY MOM DIED SHE MOVED UP HERE, FROM BAKERSFIELD. SHE SAVED ME FROM GOING INTO AN ORPHANAGE.

HERE WE ARE!

IT'S COZY, THAT'S FOR SURE. THIS IS WHERE WE EAT AND PLAY CARDS.

AND THERE'S RUPERT.

HE SLEEPS A LOT. HE'S GOT A LOT ON HIS MIND, HA HA!

WHAT'S THIS?

GRANNY'S POSTCARD COLLECTION.

BAKERSFIELD

I LOVE THESE OLD CARDS.

WHY SO MANY FROM BAKERSFIELD? IT LOOKS LIKE DULLSVILLE.
Greetings from
BAKERSFIELD
CALIFORNIA

IT'S GRANNY'S HOMETOWN. WE'RE GONNA MOVE THERE SOME DAY, BUT SHE THINKS I NEED TO STAY HERE AND FINISH SCHOOL FIRST.
I SAY WE SHOULD MOVE RIGHT AWAY!
EVEN GRANNY SAYS THIS PLACE MAKES HER FEEL TRAPPED.
BUT COME ON! LET'S GO IN MY ROOM!

HERE WE GO!
THIS IS WHERE I SLEEP.
OVER THERE ARE MY BOOKS AND GAMES.

I LOVE THIS GAME!
YEAH BUT, LET'S DO SOMETHING **TOGETHER**.
CHINESE CHECKERS?
NAH.
I HAVE AN IDEA.
WHUT?

LET'S TAKE OFF OUR CLOTHES AND HUG ONE ANOTHER.

HELL NO.
WHY NOT?

I JUST DON'T FEEL LIKE IT.

WHAT IF I PAY YOU?

TWO DOLLARS FOR TWO MINUTES!
YOU WON'T EVEN HAVE TO UNDRESS!

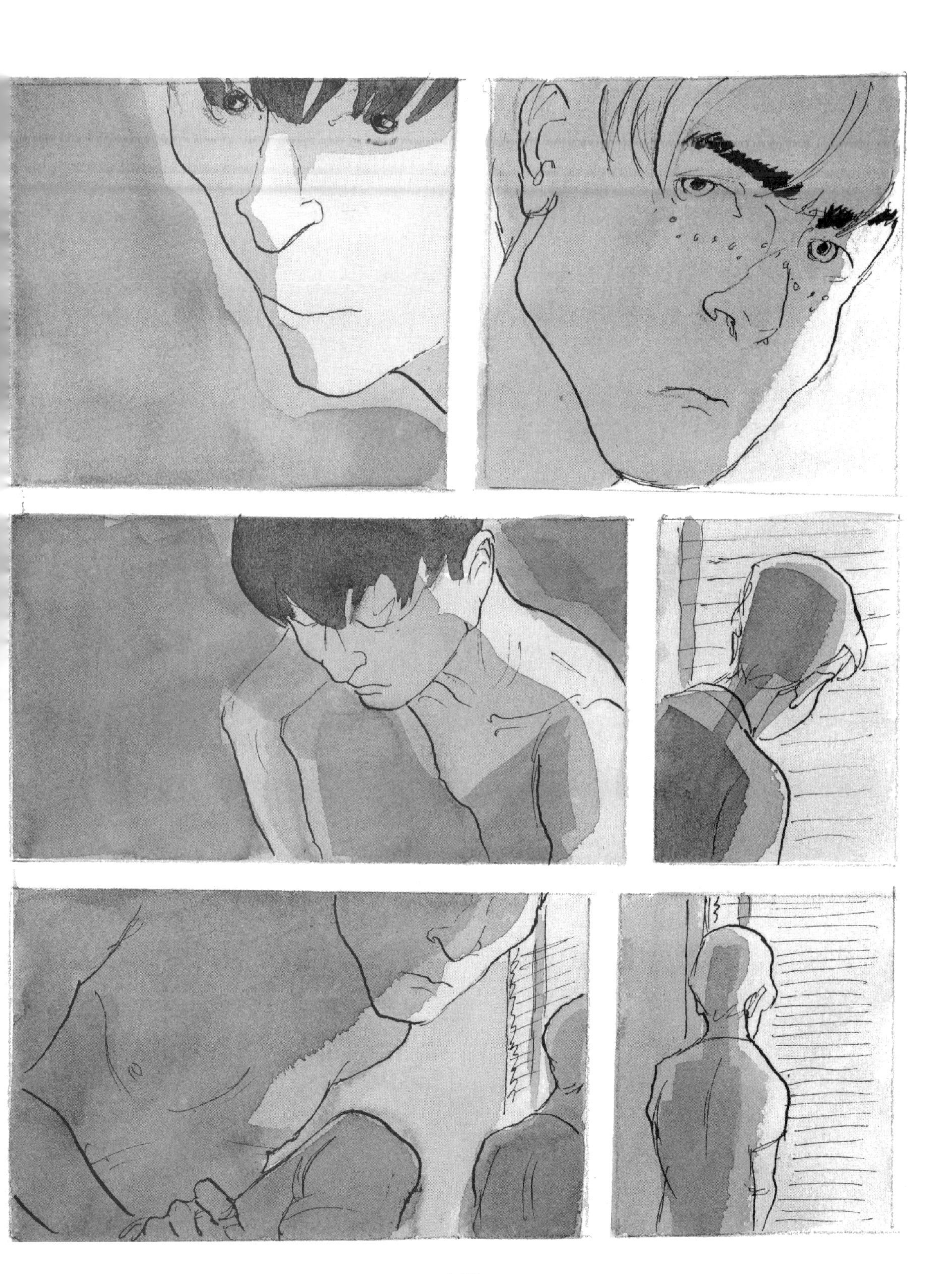

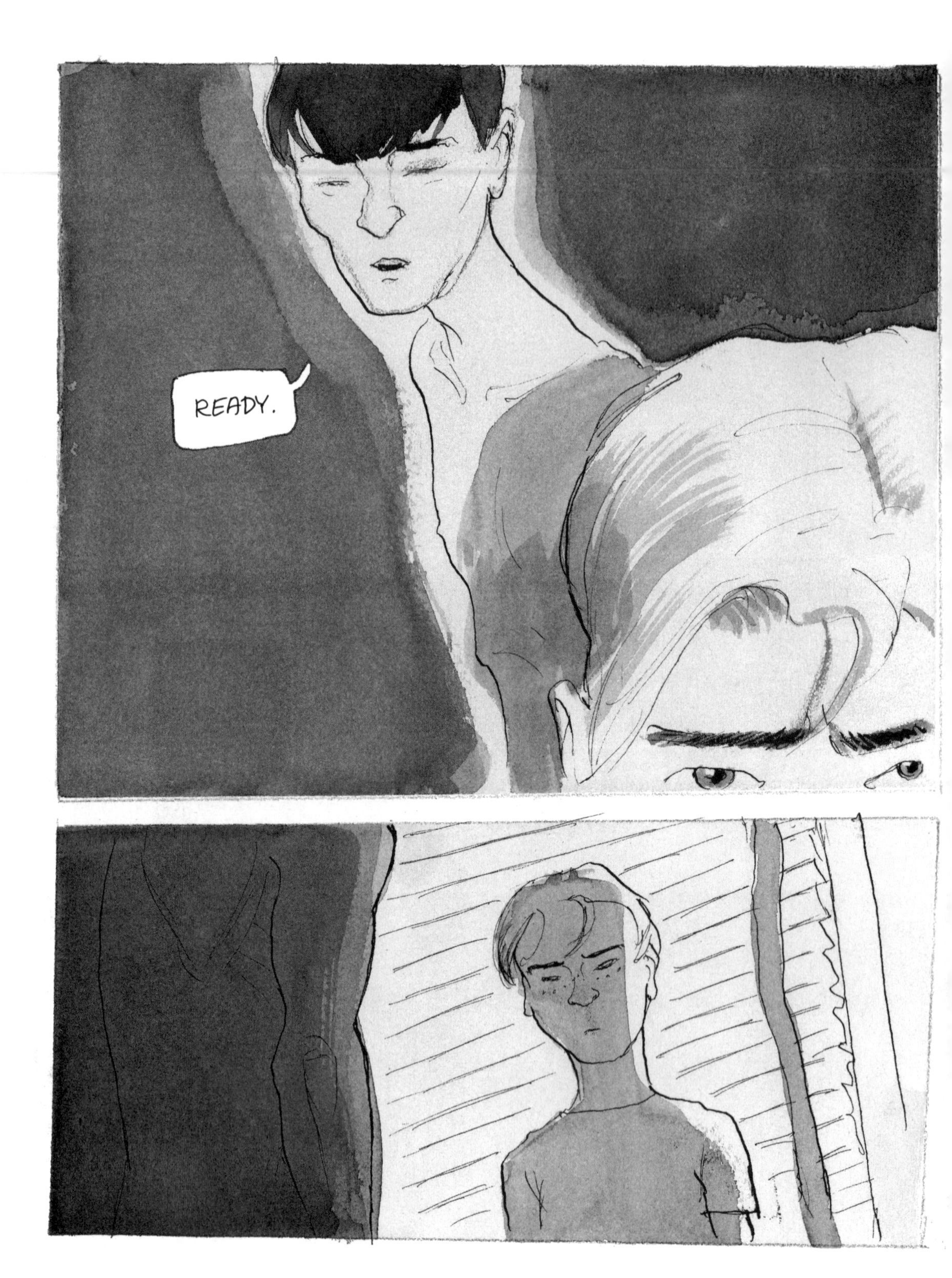
READY.

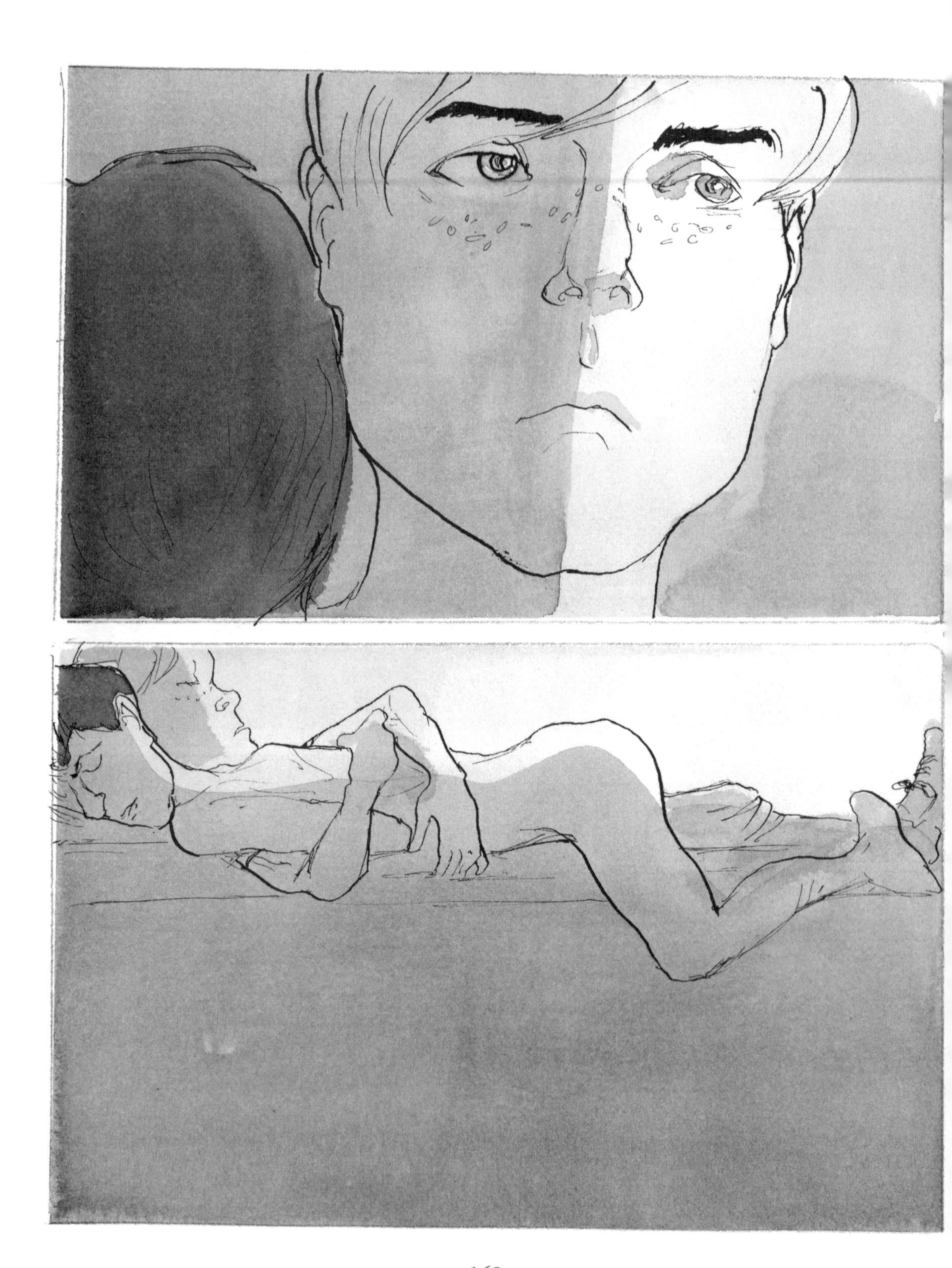

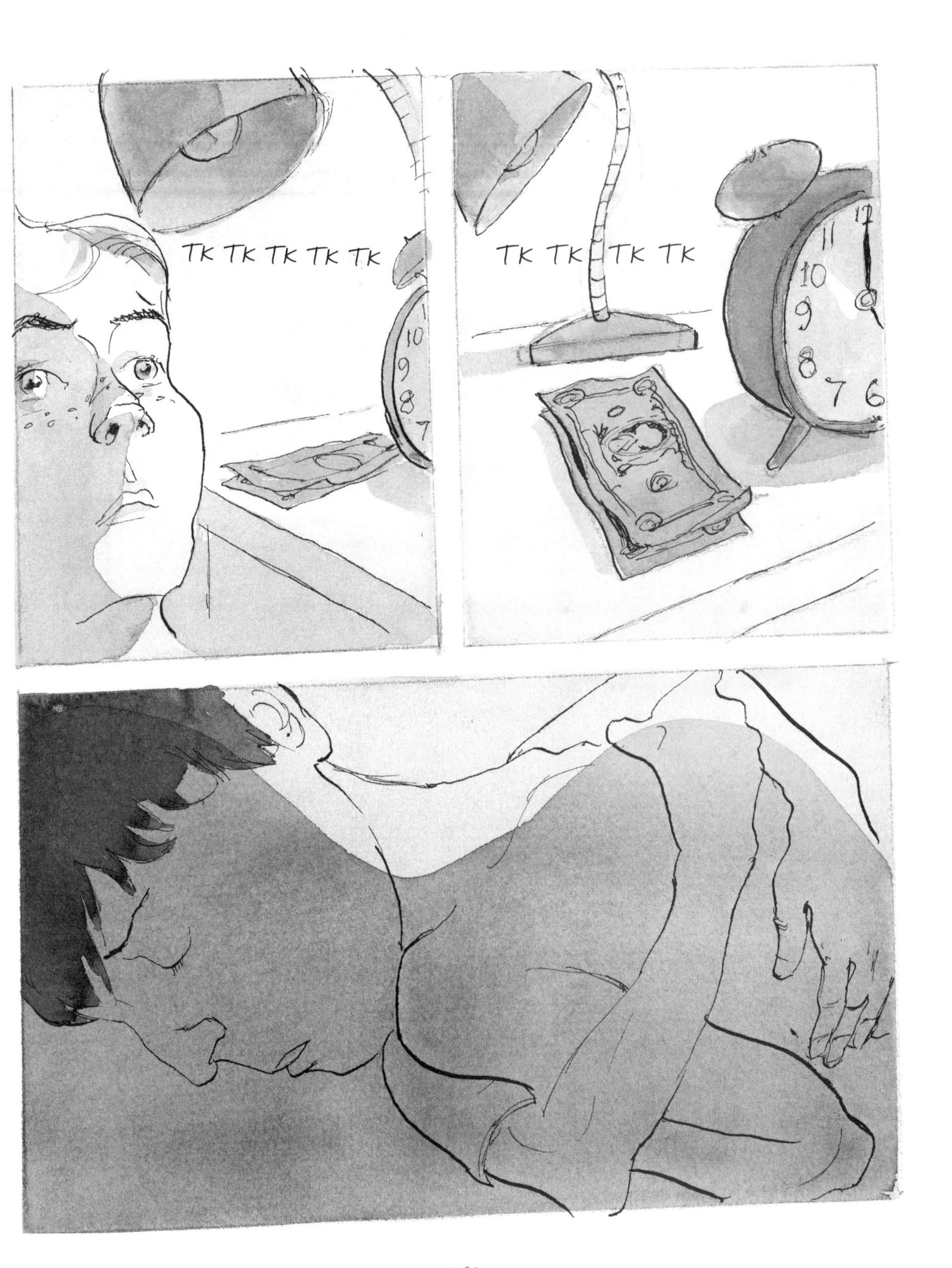
TK TK TK TK TK
TK TK TK TK

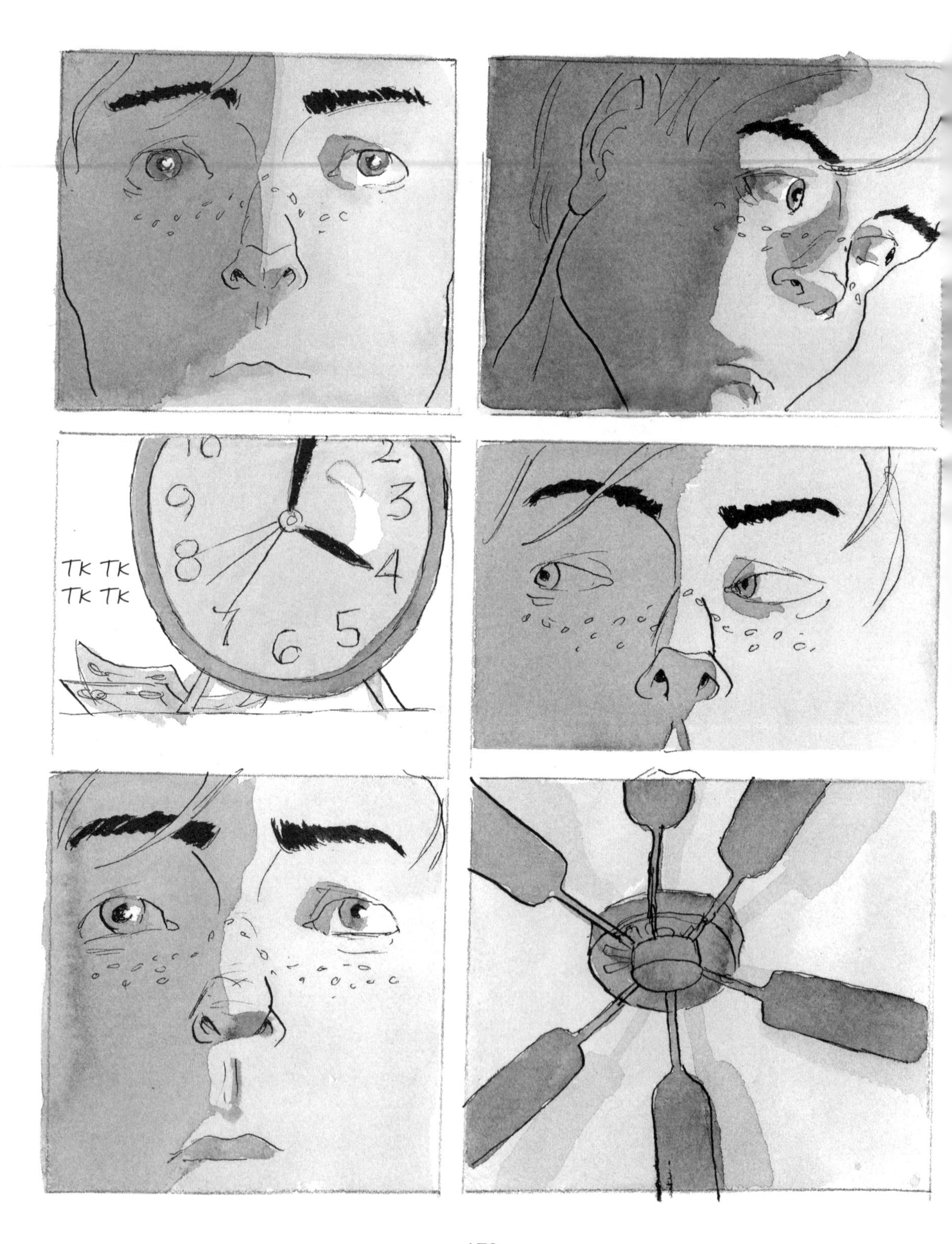
TK TK
TK TK

DRRrrriiii
iiiinnngg!

SEE YOU IN THE MORNING AT SCHOOL!

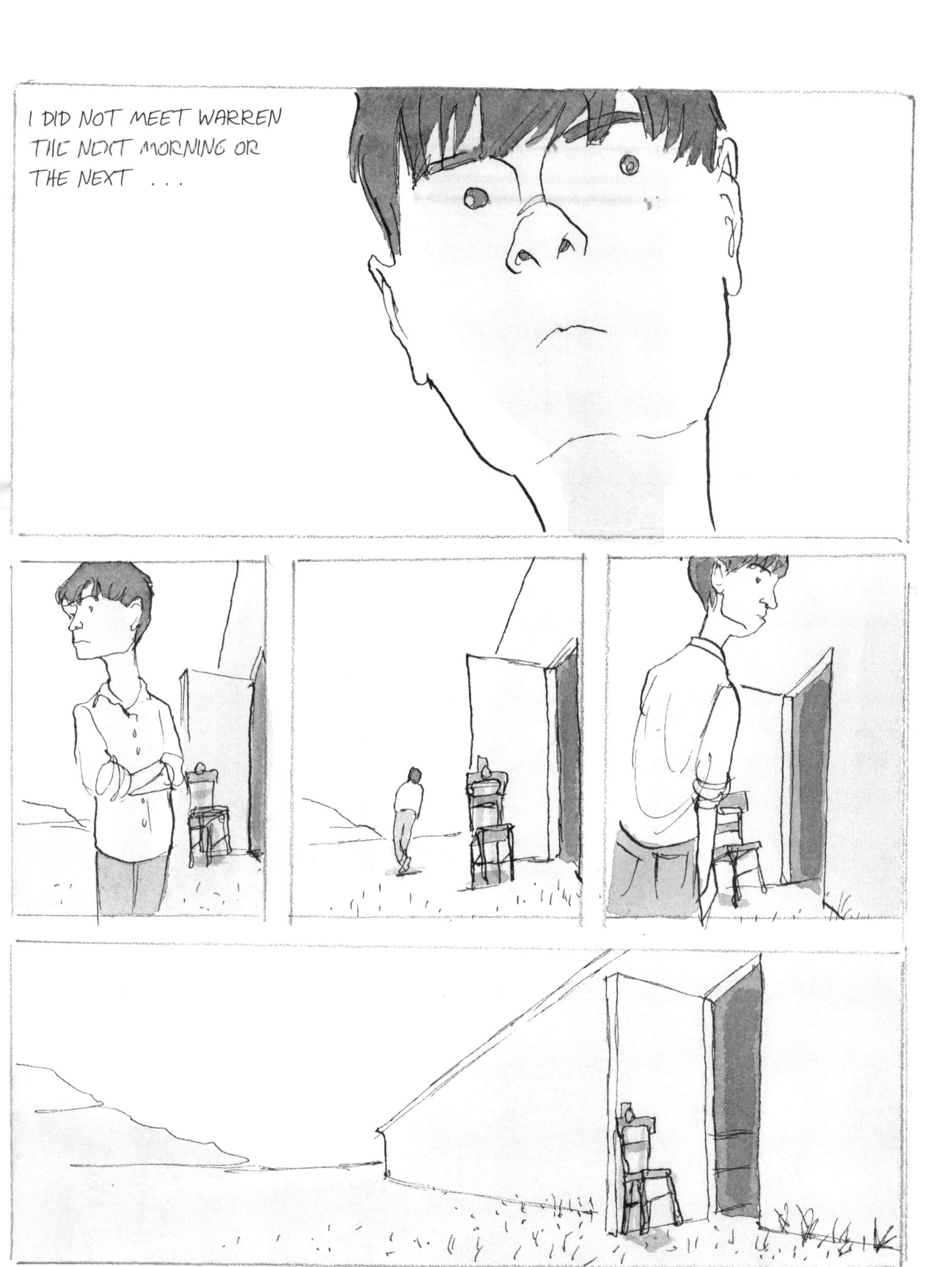
I DID NOT MEET WARREN THE NEXT MORNING OR THE NEXT . . .

. . . NOR ANY MORNING AFTER THAT. TO AVOID THE BULLIES, I CAME LATE AND TOOK THE DEMERITS.
I CHANGED MY SEAT IN CLASS TO BE FARTHER AWAY FROM HIM.

NEVERTHELESS I SPENT HIS MONEY, TO SATISFY MY SWEET TOOTH.

HEY, RUSS!

IT'S US! KURT AND WILLIE!

HEY!

LET'S GET TOGETHER! WHEN'S GOOD FOR YOU?

NOW.
NOW IS GOOD.

ARSHFIELD
ROCERY
Coca-Cola

SUMMER'S HERE! THE ARROYO AWAITS!

CHAPTER NINE

THAT WHOLE SUMMER WE WERE A UNIT, THE TREE FORT OUR HOME BASE.

UP THERE WE SMOKED OUR FIRST CIGARETTES . . .
GOT DRUNK . . .

. . . AND MADE PLENTY OF
RECONNAISSANCE MISSIONS TO
FOSTER'S DRIVE-IN, TO SEE
WHAT LAY IN OUR FUTURE.

FOSTER'S

EVERY TIME I WENT TO FOSTER'S I SENSED DANGER IN THE AIR.

BUT THE SENIOR MEATHEADS FROM SCHOOL DIDN'T EVEN RECOGNIZE ME. MAYBE IT WAS THE WHITE TEES, THE ROLLED-UP JEANS, AND THE HIGH-TOP KEDS. MAYBE IT WAS THE COMPANY I KEPT. WHATEVER IT WAS, I WAS NOW INVISIBLE.

WELL, THAT'LL BE THE DAY
WHEN YOU SAY GOODBYE . . .
'CAUSE THAT'LL BE THE DAY
WHEN I DIE.
WILLIE, YOU ARE SO FULL OF SHIT.

HOW CAN YOUR UNCLE OWN BUDDY HOLLY'S WALLET?

EASY! MY UNCLE AND BUDDY HOLLY WENT TO LUBBOCK HIGH.
BUDDY HOLLY WASN'T "BUDDY HOLLY" THEN. HE USED TO DO LEATHER-
CRAFTS AND MY UNCLE BOUGHT ONE OF HIS WALLETS AT A SCHOOL FAIR!

I STILL SAY YOU LIE LIKE A RUG, MY FRIEND.

WHAT CAN I GET FOR YOU BOYS?
HOLY MOTHER OF GOD!
I KNOW WHAT I WANT!

LOOK AT THOSE PINS!
THOSE ARE ETERNAL PINS!
HONEY, CAN I CLIMB THEM?
GIMME YOUR ORDER OR BEAT IT, YOU WORMS.

HEY. DO YOU GUYS KNOW WHAT "HAVING SEX" IS, REALLY?
IT'S GROSS!

THE MAN STICKS HIS DICK UP A WOMAN'S ASS AND TAKES A PISS!

WHO TOLD YOU THAT?

MY COUSIN. HE'S FIFTEEN!

YOUR COUSIN IS FULL OF SHIT, WILLIE.

NEXT TIME YOU SEE YOUR BRILLIANT COUSIN, ASK HIM IF HE KNOWS WHAT "PUSSY" IS!

KURT WAS THE MAN. HE KNEW ALL THE FORMS, THE BRANDS, AND THE MYSTERY LINGO THAT MALENESS SEEMED TO ASK OF US.

Tutti Frutti, oh Rutti.

A WOP-BOP-a-LOO-BOP
A WOP-

BAM!

BOOM!

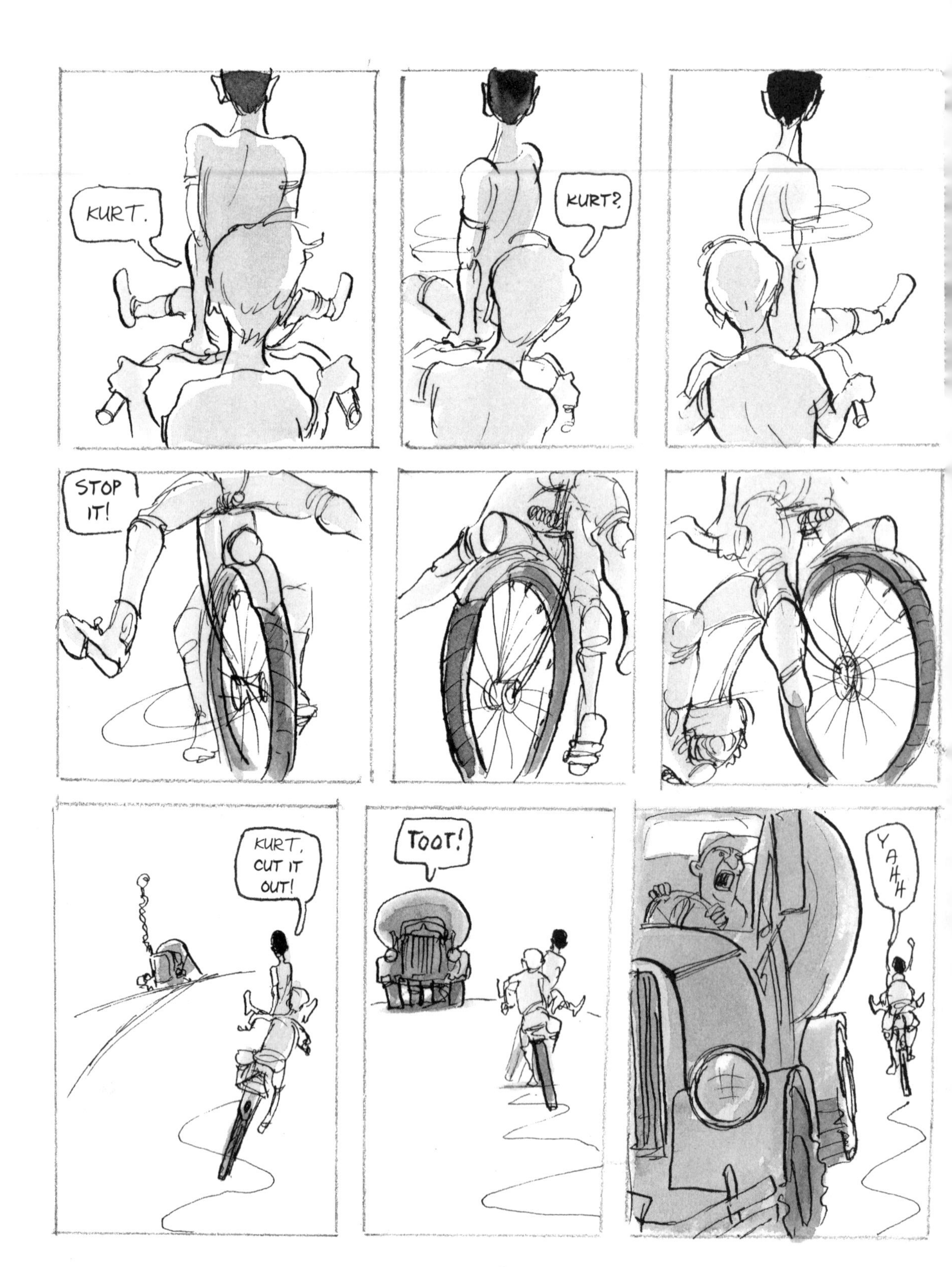
KURT.
KURT?
STOP IT!
KURT, CUT IT OUT!
TOOT!
YAHH

...HOOOOOOOOOO!
GAS

YOU'RE

CRA-

-ZY!!

HAHAHAHA!

WERE YOU TRYING TO KILL US?

OH, COME ON, MAN. ADMIT THAT WAS FUN!

OH SHIT.

MY BIKE!

THE HEAD-LAMP IS BUSTED!
BIG FUCKIN' DEAL.

OKAY. KURT WAS A REAL S.O.B., BUT I WASN'T ABOUT TO END IT WITH HIM OVER A DUSTED HEADLAMP.

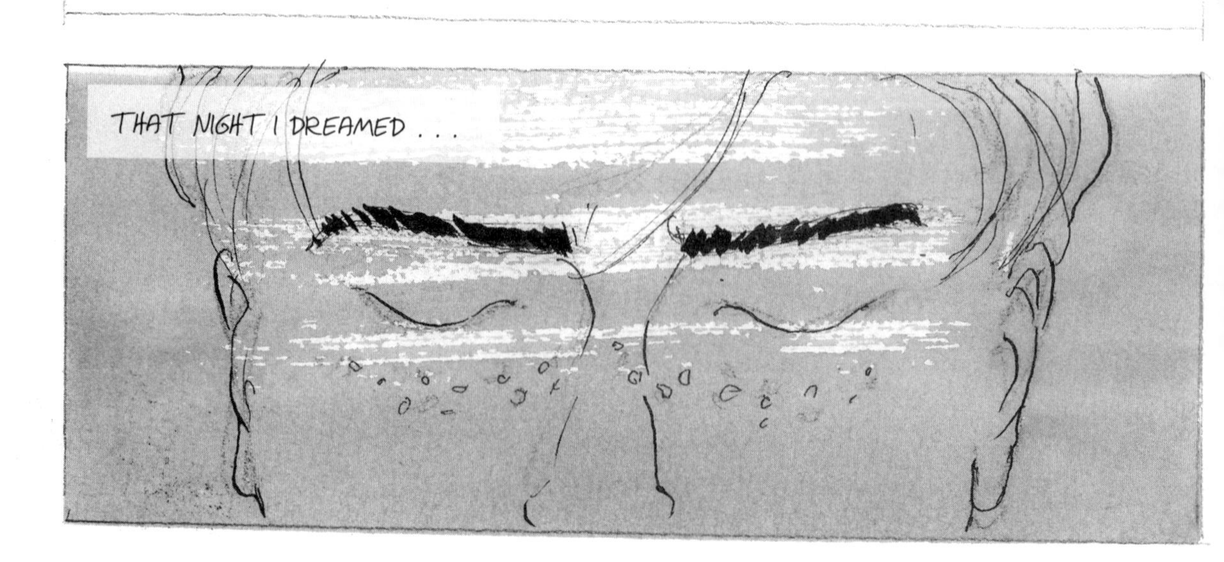
THAT NIGHT I DREAMED . . .

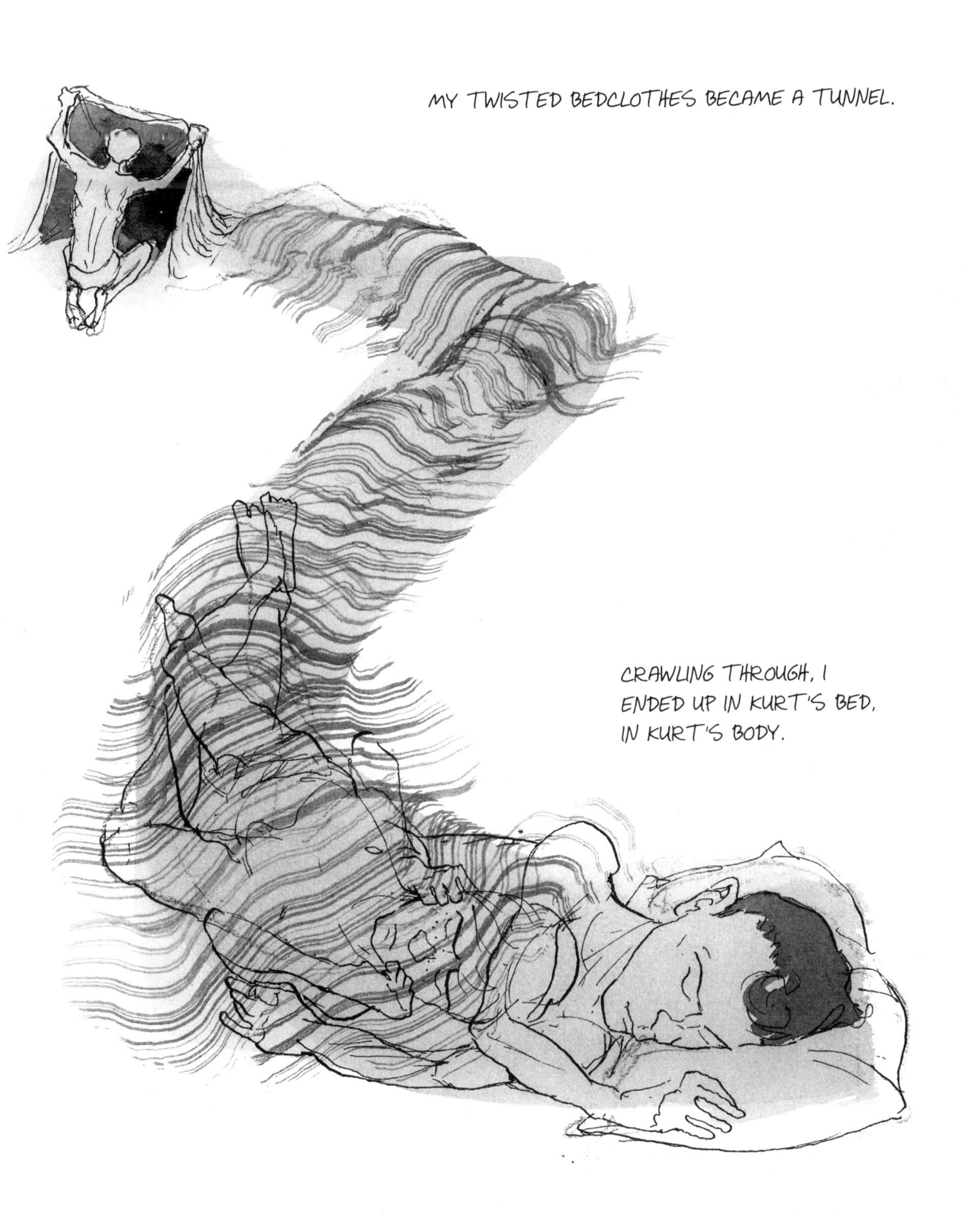
MY TWISTED BEDCLOTHES BECAME A TUNNEL.
CRAWLING THROUGH, I ENDED UP IN KURT'S BED, IN KURT'S BODY.

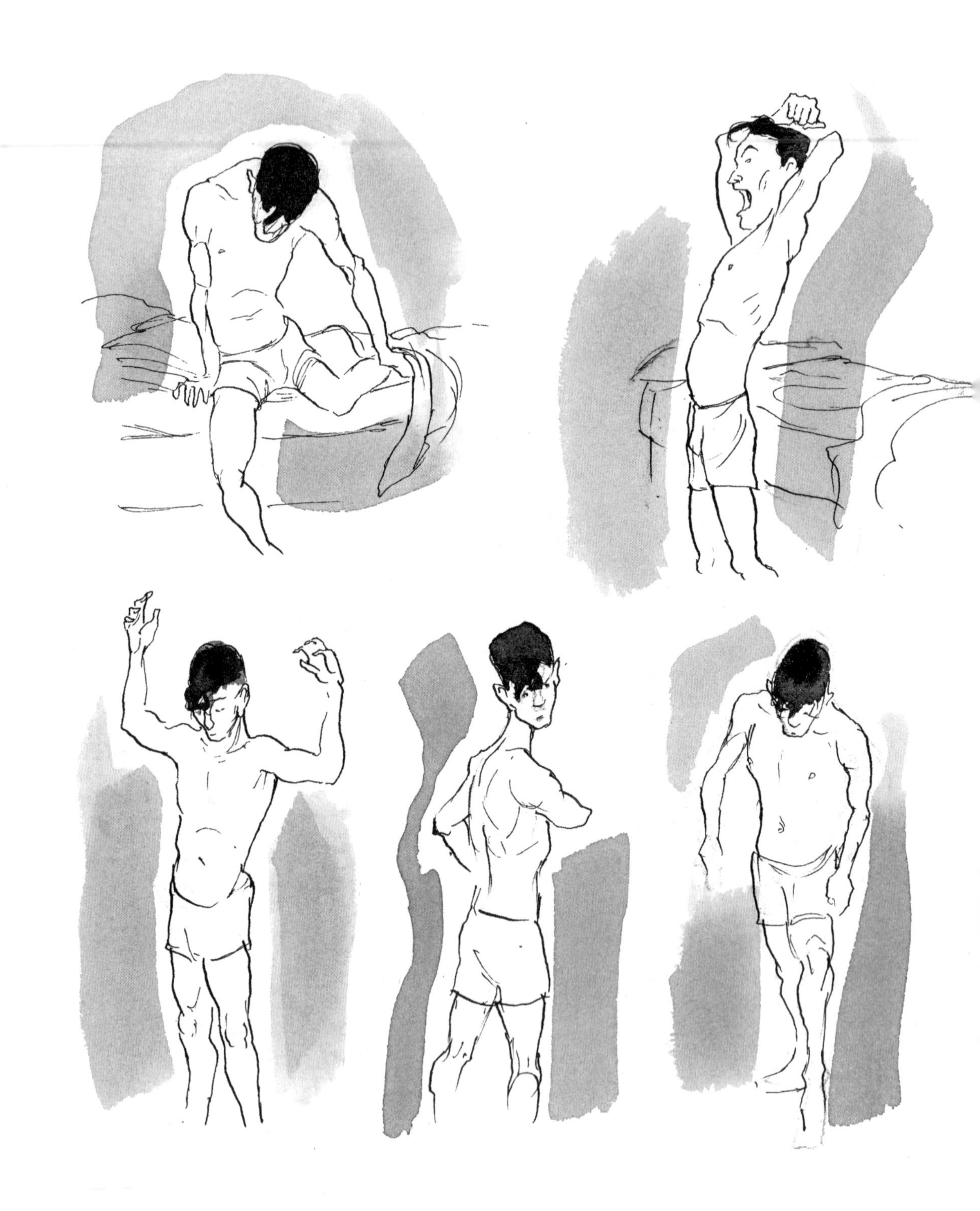

IF KURT KNEW
OF THIS SICK
DREAM . . .

CHAPTER TEN

LET'S PLAY BALL!

WE CALLED OUR FAVORITE GAME "TUNNEL BALL." THE RULES WERE SIMPLE: ONE MAN WAS THE PITCHER AND ALSO THE CATCHER. IF THE BATTER SMACKED THE BALL INTO THE TUNNEL, THE PITCHER HAD TO GO IN AND FIND IT IN THAT DANK, DARK, SMELLY PLACE.
THE THIRD GUY WAS THE AUDIENCE. HIS JOB WAS TO HECKLE EVERYBODY.

WAK

IN THE TUNNEL! IN THE TUNNEL!

GO ON, WILLIE! IN THE TUNNEL!

GRRR.

GET A MOVE ON, WILL, YOU FAGGOT!

WILLIE CAN'T FIND HIS OWN ASS USING BOTH HANDS!
COME ON, WILL.

WHO IS THAT?

ISN'T THAT McCAW?

WHAT'RE YOU LOOKING AT, COCKSUCKER?

RUSS. YOUR TURN TO PITCH.
GIVE HIM A SEC.
HE'S HANKERING AFTER HIS BUDDY.
RIGHT, RUSS?
ISN'T THAT YOUR OLD ASSHOLE BUDDY?
UP YOURS, KURT.
WHOA! HOW UNKIND! I THOUGHT IT WENT UP **YOURS**.

WHOOPS! I THINK I HIT A NERVE!

OKAY, GIRLS. LET'S PLAY BALL.

YOU TRYIN' TO
KILL ME, PRUITT?

SORRY.

WHY I DID IT, I CAN'T REALLY SAY, BUT ONE NIGHT, IN A MOMENT OF DRUNKEN EARNESTNESS, I HAD TOLD KURT AND WILLIE ABOUT WARREN AND THE HUGGING THING.

WILL YOU BLOW ME FOR A QUARTER?
WAIT. I THINK I'VE GOT A QUARTER.
COME ON, MAN! I'M ALL READY!
WHAT DID I SAY?
I'LL SEE YOU RETARDS LATER.

RUSS! PAL! DON'T LEAVE ME HERE WITH BLUE BALLS! IT'S NOT NICE!

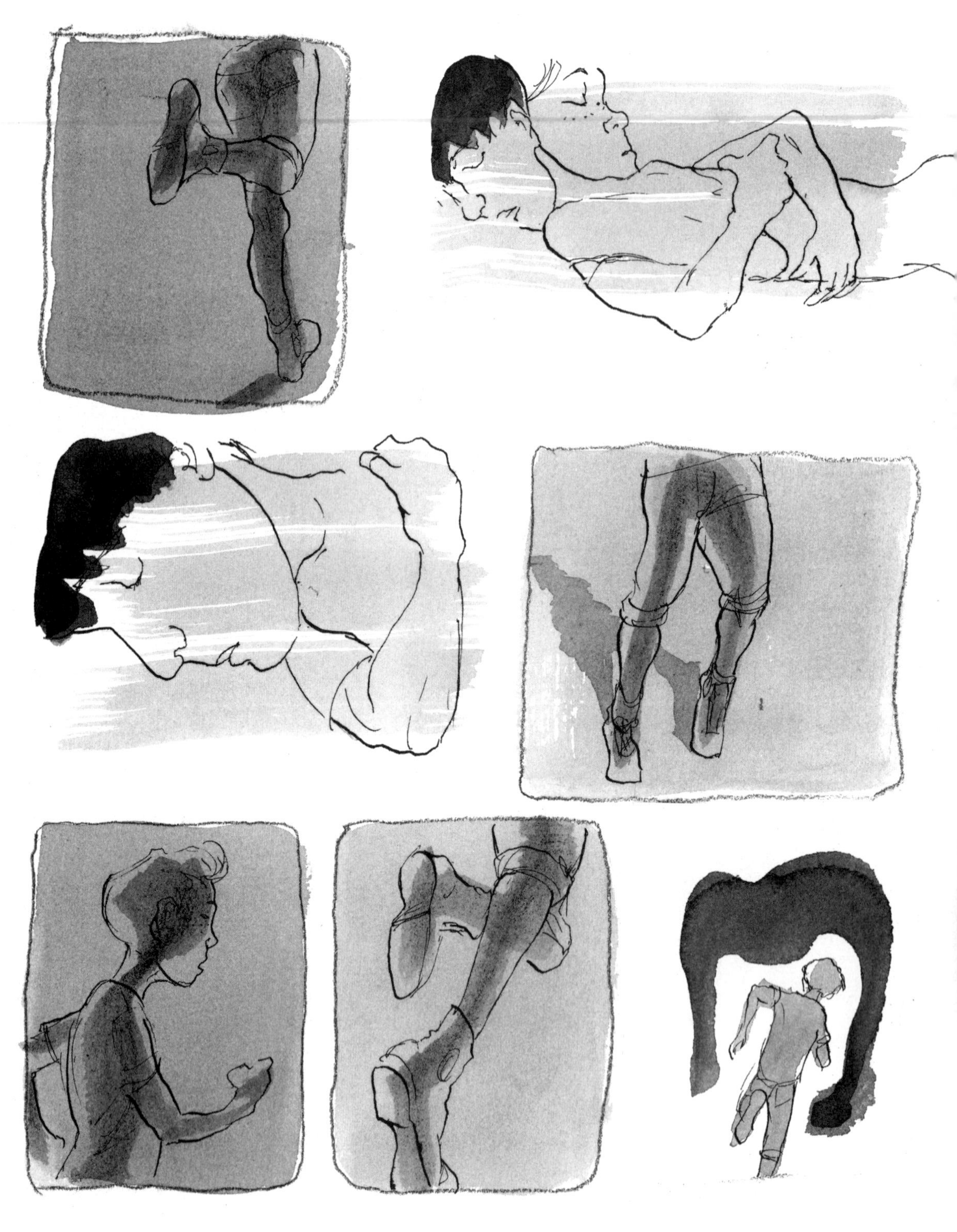

SO, THIS WAS THE PRICE YOU PAID
FOR LETTING THE WORLD IN.

A SINGLE MISSTEP, A WRONG WORD,
AND YOU'RE A REJECT, A FREAK.

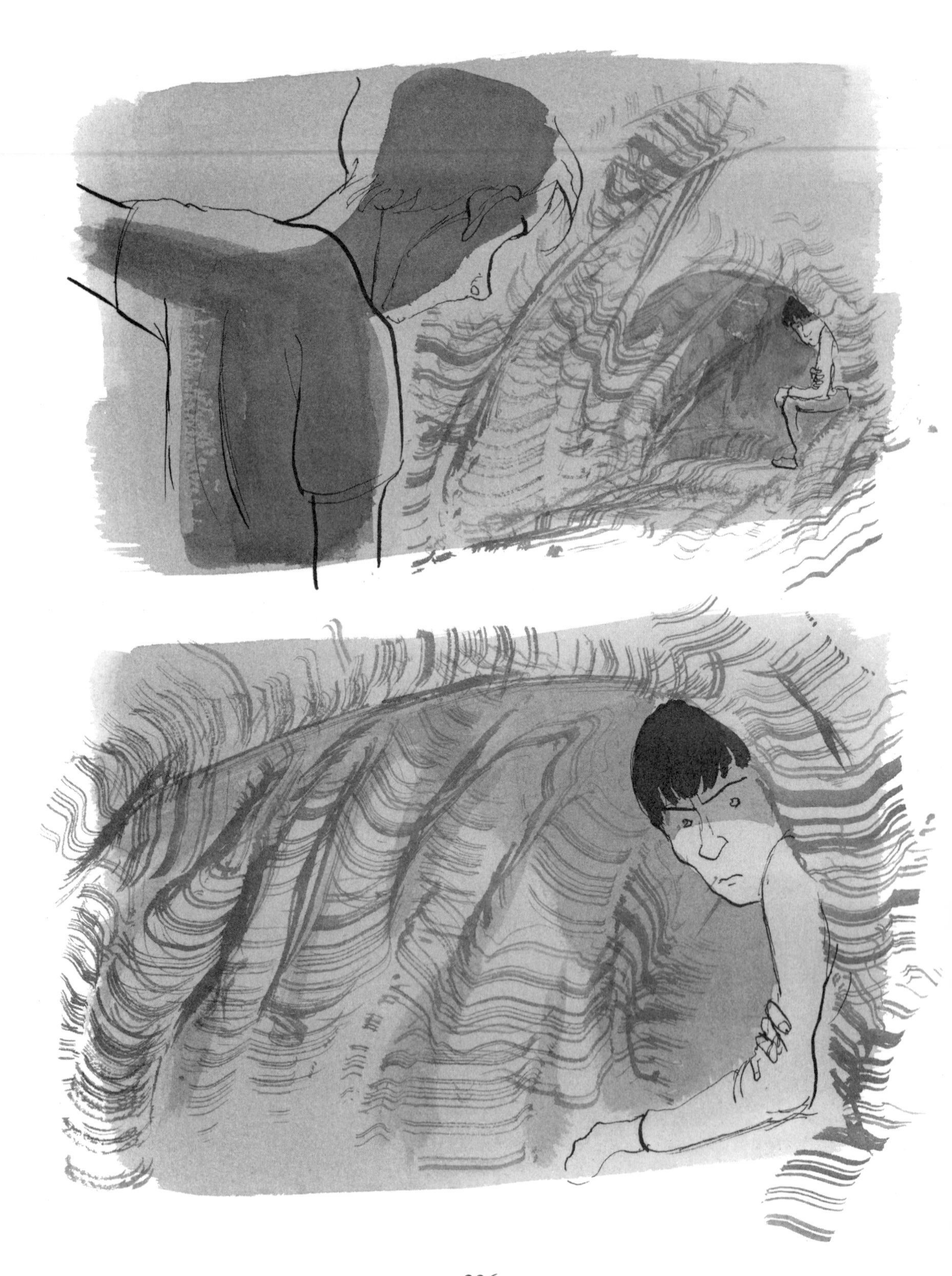

CHAPTER ELEVEN

ANY FURTHER QUESTIONS
AND COMMENTS ABOUT MY
MASCULINITY WERE PUT ON
HOLD WHEN MY DAD TOOK
ME, KURT, AND WILLIE TO
LITTLE CHINA HARBOR FOR A
WEEKEND CAMPING TRIP.

HEY, GUYS. DO YOU KNOW THIS ONE?

LEPROSEEEEE
I think I've got
LEPROSY.

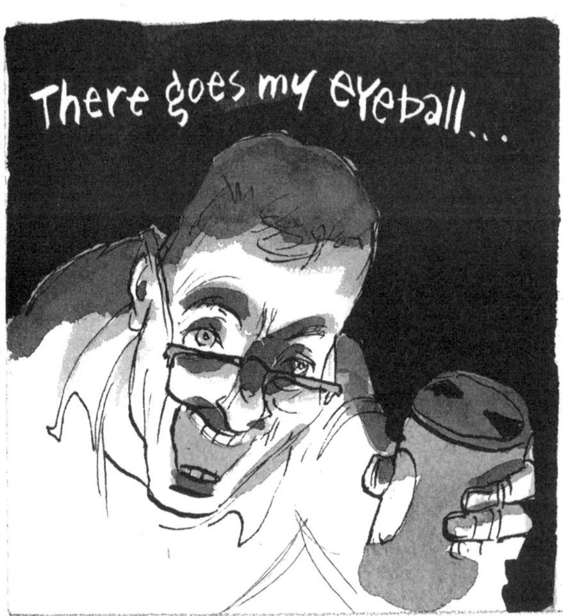
There goes my eyeball...

...into your
Highball.

HA HA HA HA HA

PRETTY COOL DAD YOU'VE GOT THERE!

"LEPROSEEE! I THINK I'VE GOT LEPROSY!"

NEXT DAY, DAD TOOK US DOWN TO THE HARBOR FOR LUNCH.
"THERE GOES MY THUMB, DEAR . . . INTO YOUR RUM, DEAR!"

"THERE GOES MY CHIN, INTO YOUR GIN!"

PARKING FOR
MAH'S
MAH'S
SHRIMP, CRAB
BEER & WINE

HEY, WEN!

MIKE! HOW NICE TO SEE YOU!
HELLO, RUSSELL!

HI, MRS. MAH!

EVERYBODY HUNGRY?
SORRY, I HAVE NO ROOM ON THE DECK. PLEASE, SIT IN HERE WITH ME!

GIVE THESE GUYS WHATEVER THEY WANT.
I'LL HAVE A BEER.

FWSSSHHHH!

SO, MIKE. YOU STILL WORK AT THE SAME PLACE?
YUP.
YOU LIKE IT?
WELL, LET'S PUT IT THIS WAY: IN PUBLIC SCHOOL KIDS ACT LIKE THEY'RE IN PRISON. IN PRISON, THEY DON'T HAVE TO ACT.

YOU FIND A NICE LADY FRIEND YET?

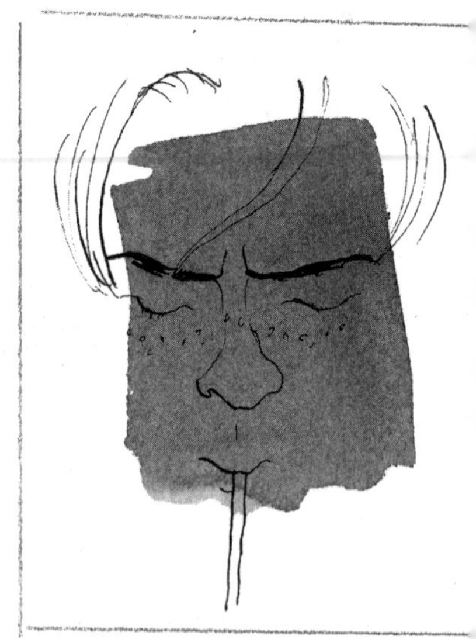

WEN, THERE AREN'T TOO MANY NICE LADIES IN SAN QUENTIN.

BUT YOU'RE STILL LOOKING, RIGHT?
FOR RUSSELL'S SAKE?
FOR YOUR OWN SAKE?

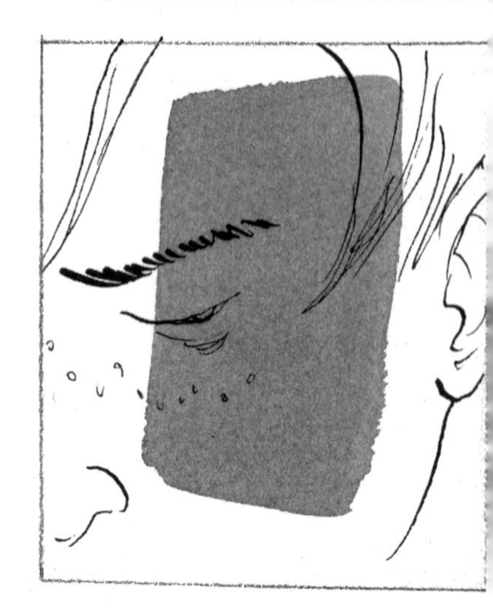

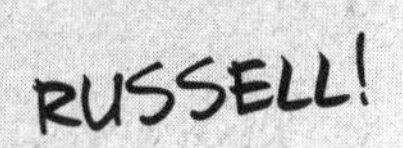
RUSSELL!

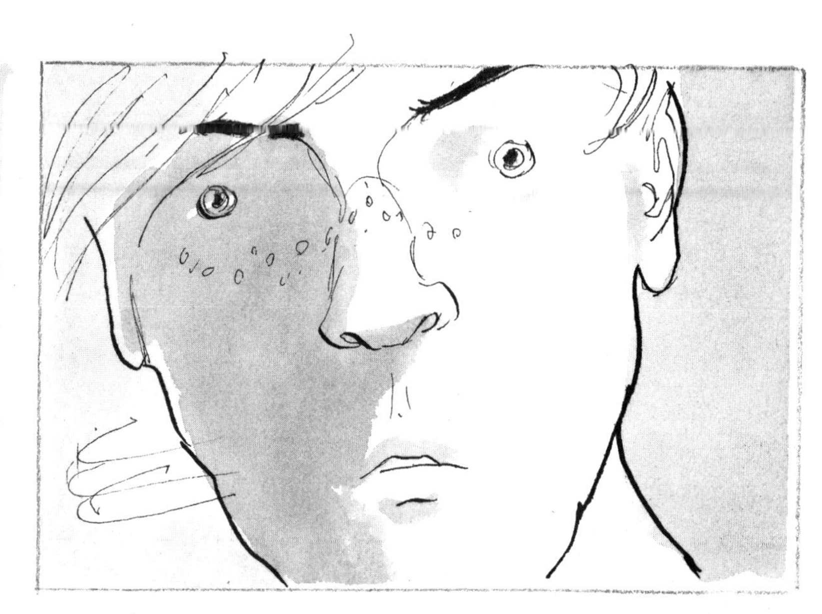

HERE. TAKE THIS. YOU AND YOUR BUDDIES SHOULD GO FOR A BOAT RIDE.

YOU LITTLE PUNKS STAY IN HARBOR, OKAY?
BOAT RENTAL 50¢ PER HOUR
HEY! I'VE GOT A NEW VERSE . . .

"LEPROSEEE! I THINK I'VE GOT LEPROSY! THERE GOES MY WEENIE . . .

"IN YOUR MARTINI!!"

HAHAHA!
HO-HO, HEE-HEE, HA-HA-HAH!

HO BOY! WE LEFT THE HARBOR!
NO SHIT!

TURN! TURN!!!

EVERYBODY GOOD?

ALL RIGHT!
LET'S GO FOR A SWIM!

LAST ONE IN IS A MO!

PLOOP
WAIT! THE BOAT!
IT'S TOO CLOSE TO THE WATER! IT'LL WASH AWAY!

COME ON, GIRL! AFRAID OF THE WATER?

IT'S A RIPTIDE!

WILLIE!

YOU GO IN THERE, YOU'LL BOTH DROWN!

AW! DON'T YOU MAKE A SWEET COUPLE?!
MAN, YOU NEVER LET UP, DO YOU?

YOU LEFT THE HARBOR!
CALM DOWN, ASSHOLE. YOUR BOAT IS FINE.

RUSSELL! JIAN WAS SENDING SOME GUYS OUT TO FIND YOU!
I'M OKAY. WE'RE FINE.

RUSSELL . . .

I WAS SO WORRIED . . .

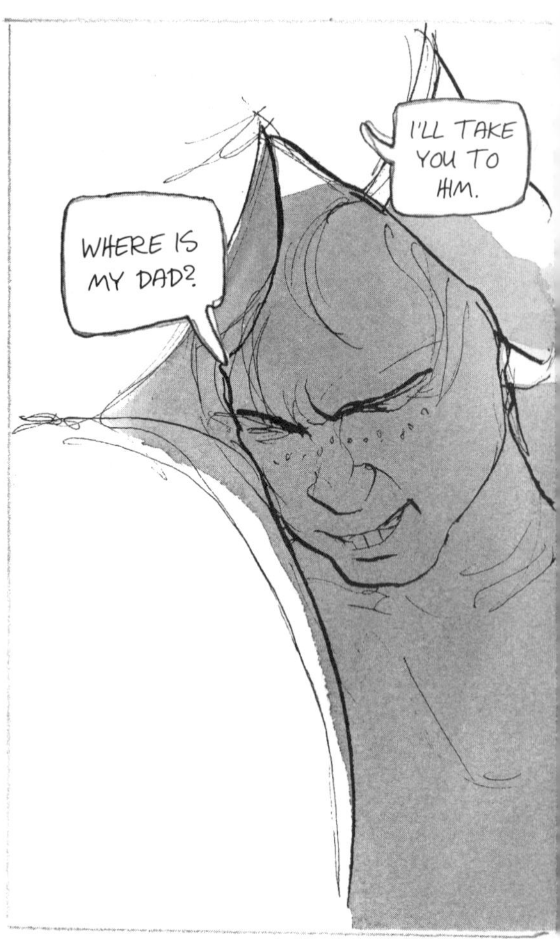
WHERE IS MY DAD?
I'LL TAKE YOU TO HIM.

MIKE.
MIKE?
RUSSELL
IS HERE.
HEY,
SON.
HOW'D IT
GO?
GOOD, I
GUESS.

TIME TO BREAK CAMP.
SHH.
WHOA!
MIKE! LET ONE OF JIAN'S GUYS DRIVE YOU HOME!
DO ANY OF YOU BOYS KNOW HOW TO DRIVE?
I DO, SIR!
FUCK OFF!

"LEPROSEE!!
I THINK I'VE GOT
LEPROSEEEE!"

"THERE GOES MY CHIN, DEAR,
INTO YOUR GIN, DEAR!"
HEH
HEH
HEH.

SEE YOU TOMORROW, RUSS!
THANKS A LOT, MR. PRUITT!

RUSSELL, LEAVE ALL THAT STUFF.
I'VE GOT TO GO LIE DOWN.

THAT WAS THE LAST TIME
I EVER SAW MY FATHER.

CHAPTER TWELVE

DAD STOPPED COMING HOME.

I STARTED TO AVOID KURT AND WILLIE AND SPENT THE EMPTY HOURS IN THE EMPTY HOUSE.
MRS. MAH'S FOOD STILL APPEARED ON THE DOORSTEP EVERY EVENING LIKE MAGIC. I LEARNED TO EAT COLD FISH AND RICE FOR BREAKFAST, LUNCH AND DINNER.

POP

DAD HAD NOT PAID THE ELECTRIC BILL.

THE WATER WAS TURNED OFF.

THE TELEPHONE LINE WAS DEAD.

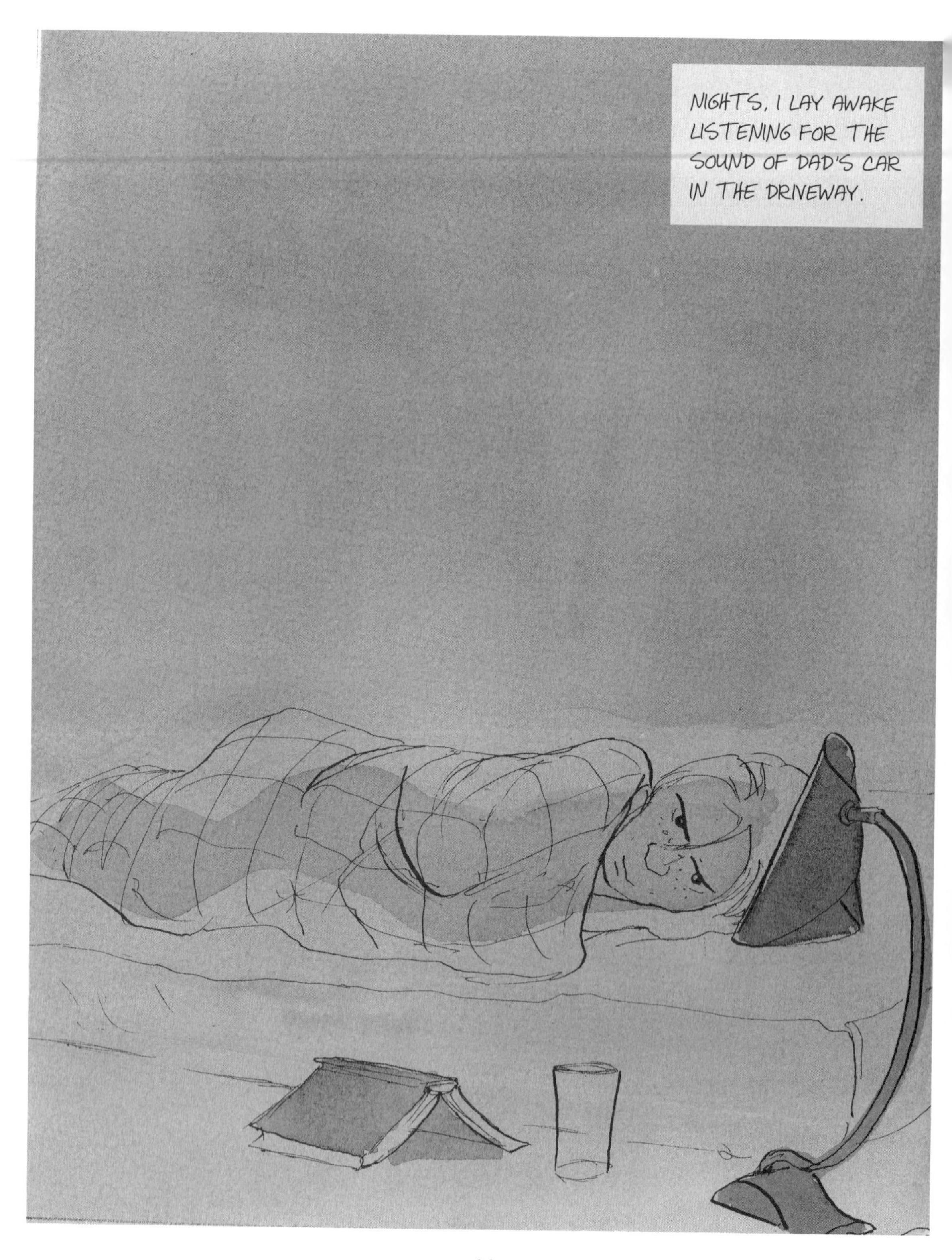
NIGHTS, I LAY AWAKE LISTENING FOR THE SOUND OF DAD'S CAR IN THE DRIVEWAY.

OKAY.
THIS WAS A SIGN.

DARKNESS. NO RUNNING WATER. A 'FRIDGE FULL OF ROTTING FOOD. FRIENDS WHO WERE NOT REALLY FRIENDS.

I HAD TO GET OUT. KURT, WILLIE, AND I HAD STOPPED GOING TO THE TREE FORT. I WOULD SLEEP THERE TONIGHT.

-BRAKE!
DAD?!

MAIL
MIKE?
HELLO?

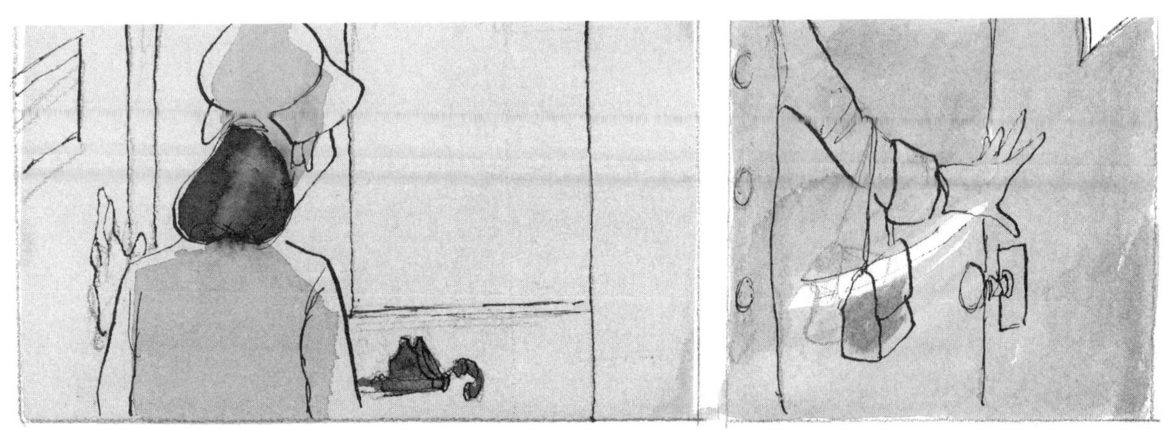

ANYONE HOME?

MRS. MAH?

RUSSELL! I'M SORRY TO DISTURB YOU. I KNOCKED. THE FRONT DOOR WAS OPEN, SO . . .

I'VE BEEN SO CONCERNED. I HAVEN'T HEARD FROM YOUR FATHER FOR SO LONG . . .

I'VE BEEN CALLING YOU EVERY DAY. YOUR LINE IS DEAD.
RUSSELL, THIS HOUSE IS A PIGSTY!

WHERE IS YOUR FATHER?

I DUNNO.

HE HASN'T CALLED YOU? NOT LEFT A NOTE?
NO.

WHAT HAPPENED TO THE LIGHTS?

IT SMELLS AWFUL IN HERE!
AND JUST LOOK AT THAT PILE OF MAIL!

RUSSELL. LISTEN TO ME. THIS IS NOT RIGHT. I WANT YOU TO PACK SOME THINGS AND COME STAY WITH US.
I WILL COME BACK FOR YOU AFTER WORK. SIX O'CLOCK.

YOU HEAR WHAT I'M SAYING?
I'LL BE BACK AT SIX TONIGHT.
OKAY?
'K.
PROMISE?
PROMISE.

I HATED TO BREAK MY PROMISE TO MRS. MAH, BUT I ALREADY HAD MY PLANS.

I NEVER WANTED TO SEE THIS HOUSE, THIS STREET, THIS TOWN, EVER AGAIN.

I WOULD SLEEP THAT NIGHT IN THE TREE FORT. THEN, TOMORROW, I WOULD BIKE TO ALASKA. I WOULD LIVE AMONG THE ESKIMOS. NO ONE WOULD KNOW ME. NO ONE COULD SPEAK TO ME. I WOULD START ALL OVER. EVERYTHING THERE WOULD BE FRESH, OPEN, CLEAN AND FREE.

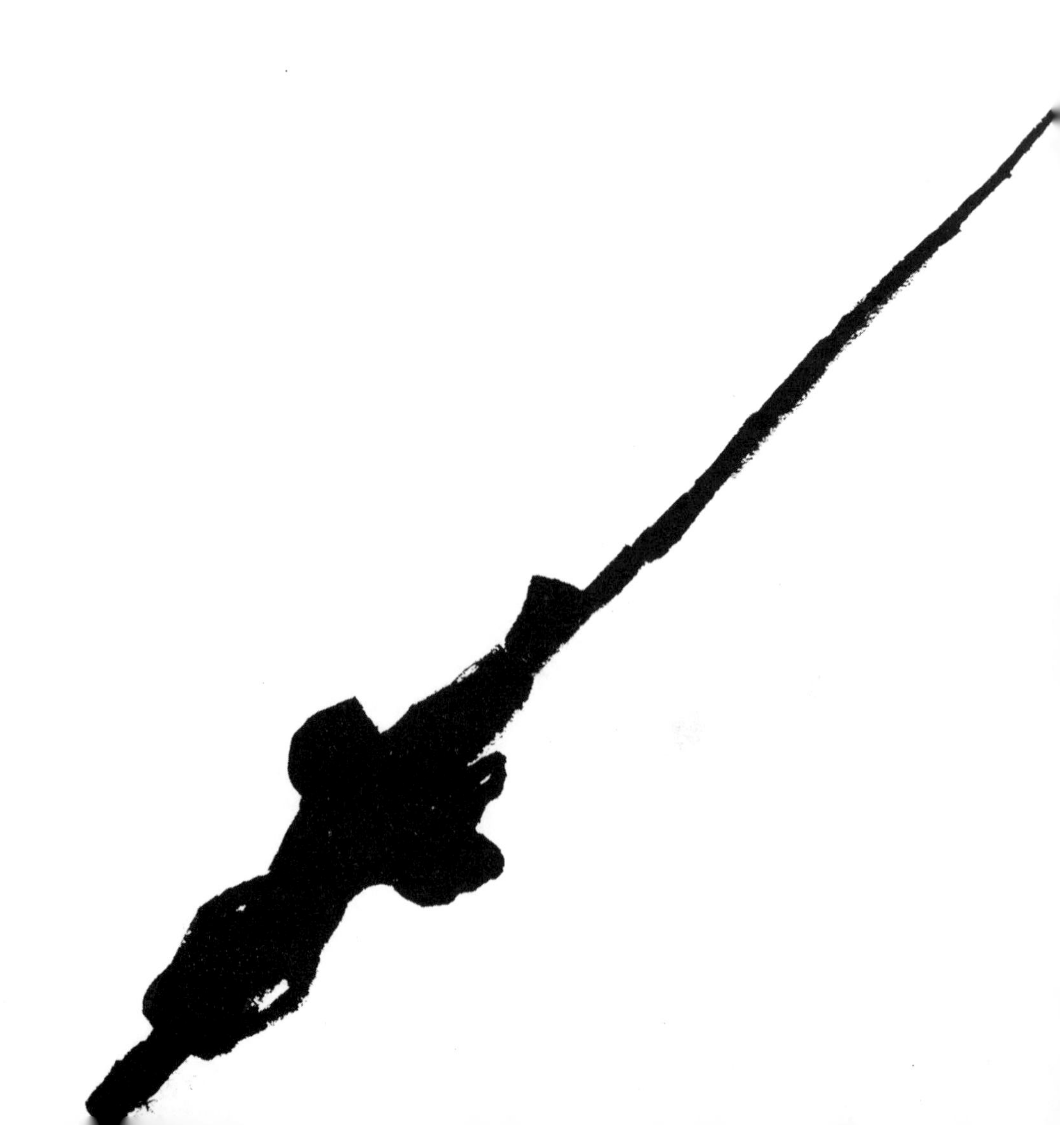

CHAPTER THIRTEEN

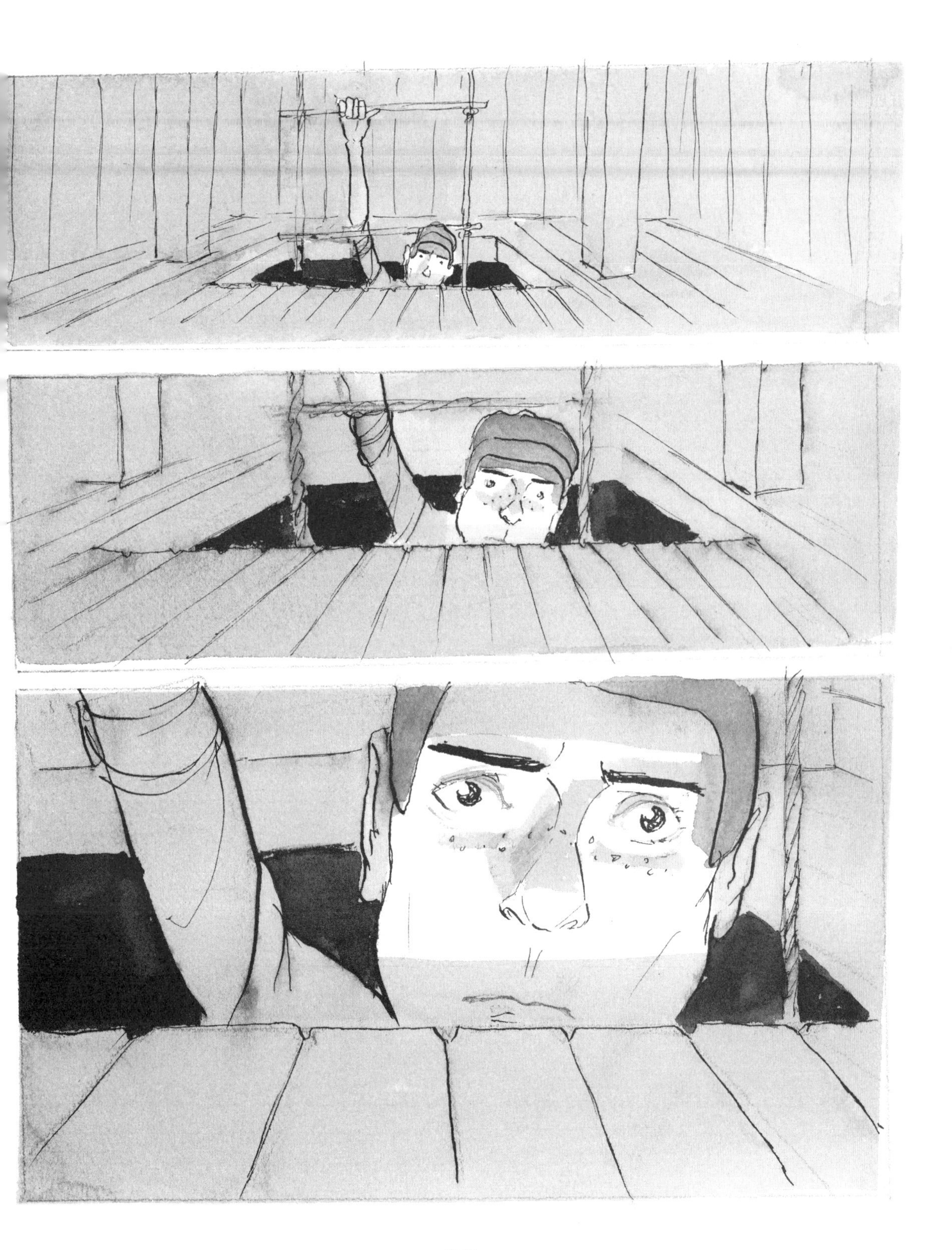

IS THAT IT?

GET OFFA ME!

YOU SURE PROMISE A LOT BUT YOU DON'T DELIVER MUCH!
YEAH? YOU SHOULD TRY ME WHEN I HAVEN'T HAD SO MUCH TO DRINK!
NO, THANKS. NOT INTERESTED.

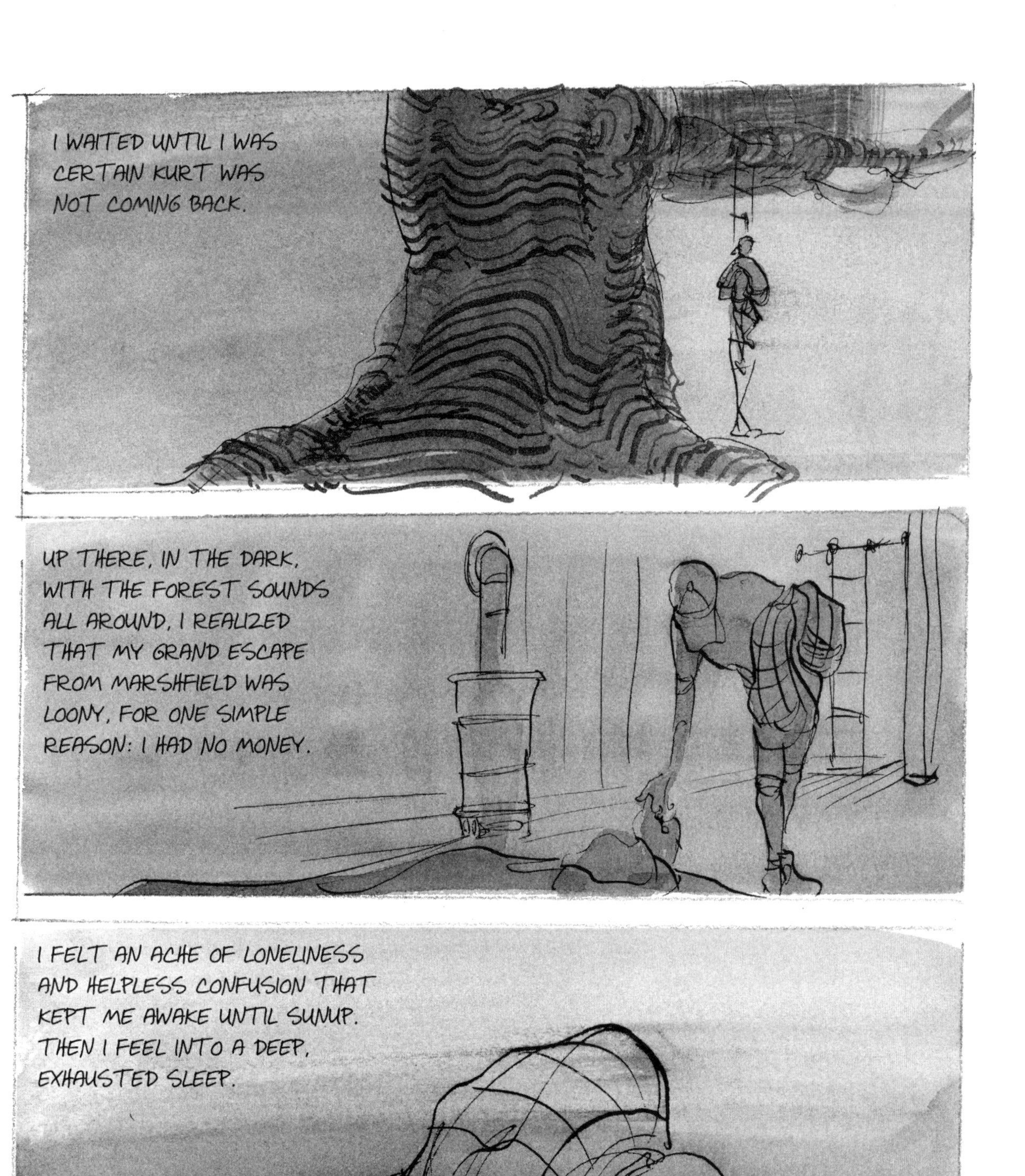
I WAITED UNTIL I WAS CERTAIN KURT WAS NOT COMING BACK.
UP THERE, IN THE DARK, WITH THE FOREST SOUNDS ALL AROUND, I REALIZED THAT MY GRAND ESCAPE FROM MARSHFIELD WAS LOONY, FOR ONE SIMPLE REASON: I HAD NO MONEY.
I FELT AN ACHE OF LONELINESS AND HELPLESS CONFUSION THAT KEPT ME AWAKE UNTIL SUNUP. THEN I FEEL INTO A DEEP, EXHAUSTED SLEEP.

HEY! THERE YOU ARE!
WE SAW YOUR BIKE BACK THERE ON THE PATH.
WHERE'VE YOU BEEN LATELY?
JUST TAKING A BREAK, I GUESS.
FROM WHAT?
OH, YOU KNOW.
KURT.
THAT'S JUST KURT BEING A DICK.
HE CAN'T HELP HIMSELF.
HE STILL LIKES YOU.

WE WERE JUST ON OUR WAY TO THE ARROYO.
ONE LAST GAME OF TUNNEL BALL BEFORE SUMMER ENDS.
JOIN US!

HURRY UP!

WHAT'S GOING ON?

YOU LIVE UP THERE NOW?

I JUST SPENT THE NIGHT.

SOMETHING WRONG?

LOOKS LIKE THE QUEER WITH THE GUN IS BECOMING A REGULAR FIXTURE AROUND HERE.

SHALL WE?
I'M AT BAT. RUSSELL, YOU PITCH.
STRIKE HIM OUT, RUSS.

OOH! OUCH!
KRAK
IN THE TUNNEL! IN THE TUNNEL!

WE ALL KNOW WHO DID THIS!

McCAW!!

McCAW, YOU MOTHER FUCKER!

HE MUST BE HIDING.

IF HE HEARD YOU SCREAMING HIS NAME LIKE A MANIAC, SURE AS SHIT HE'S HIDING.

WATCH FOR HIM. I'LL BE RIGHT BACK.

KURT. WHAT THE FUCK, MAN?
STAY UP THERE. I'LL BE BACK IN A SEC.

WE HAVE TO CALL THE POLICE.

THE COPS. KURT WOULD TELL THEM WARREN DID IT. I'D HAVE TO GO AGAINST HIM.
I KNEW WARREN WOULDN'T HURT ANYTHING.

BUT KURT SAID NOTHING ABOUT WARREN.

I GUESS THIS'LL TEACH YOU LITTLE PUNKS TO QUIT PLAYING IN THIS STINKHOLE.

WHAT ABOUT THE DOGS?
WHAT ABOUT THEM?
YOU WANT ME TO GET A PRIEST? GIVE 'EM THEIR LAST RITES?

I ONLY MEANT THEIR OWNERS WILL BE WORRIED.

WELL, THAT DOES PRESENT A PROBLEM. ALL THEM DOGS ARE WEARING COLLARS WITH NO TAGS.
THAT PSYCHO TOOK THEM SO HE CAN'T BE TRAILED.
SON, YOU SHOULD CONSIDER A FUTURE IN DETECTIVE WORK.

"WHAT ABOUT THE DOGGIES?"
MAN, YOU SURE MADE US LOOK LIKE A BUNCH OF SISSIES DOWN THERE.
SOMEHOW KURT ALWAYS MANAGED TO COME OUT THE WINNER.

WITH NO OTHER PLACE TO GO THAT NIGHT, I WENT TO THE MAHS'.
MORE, RUSSELL?
THANK YOU.
告诉他这个。
每个男孩都需要一些“走路”钱
MR. MAH SAYS TAKE THIS. HE SAYS, "A YOUNG MAN NEEDS SOME 'WALKING-AROUND' MONEY."

WHY WERE THESE STRANGERS
BEING SO KIND TO ME? THEY HAD
NO IDEA WHAT A WORTHLESS
SHIT I REALLY WAS.

CHAPTER FOURTEEN

FOSTER'S

FOSTER'S

Foster's
Foster's
WILLIE, I'VE BEEN MEANING TO ASK. ARE YOU SERIOUSLY TRYING TO GROW A 'STACHE?
GIVE IT THREE YEARS, IT MIGHT HAVE SIX HAIRS ON IT.
WHAT CAN I GET YOU FELLOWS?

YOU CAN START BY GETTING US ANOTHER WAITRESS.

A BETTER-LOOKING ONE.

GLAD TO, TINY TIM.

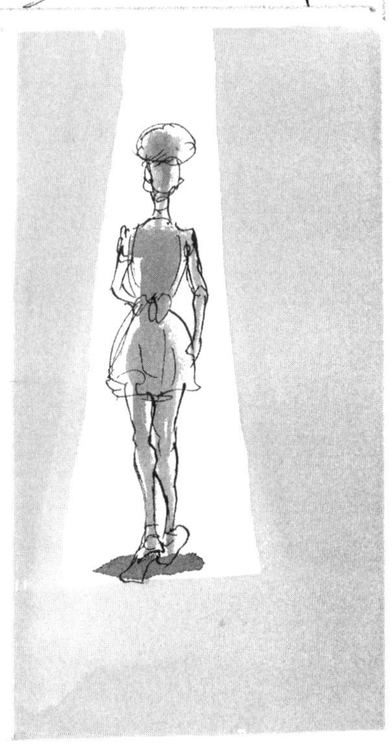

WHAT WAS THAT ALL ABOUT?

I CAN'T STAND LOOKING AT THAT SLAG.

SO WHAT? THAT'S NO WAY TO TALK TO ANYONE.

I GUESS I CAN TALK TO HER ANY WAY I LIKE, WILL.

HOLD THE PHONE. WHAT'S THIS?
'SCUSE ME. I'LL BE RIGHT BACK.
WHERE ARE YOU GOING?
THERE IS A FUNGUS AMONG US.

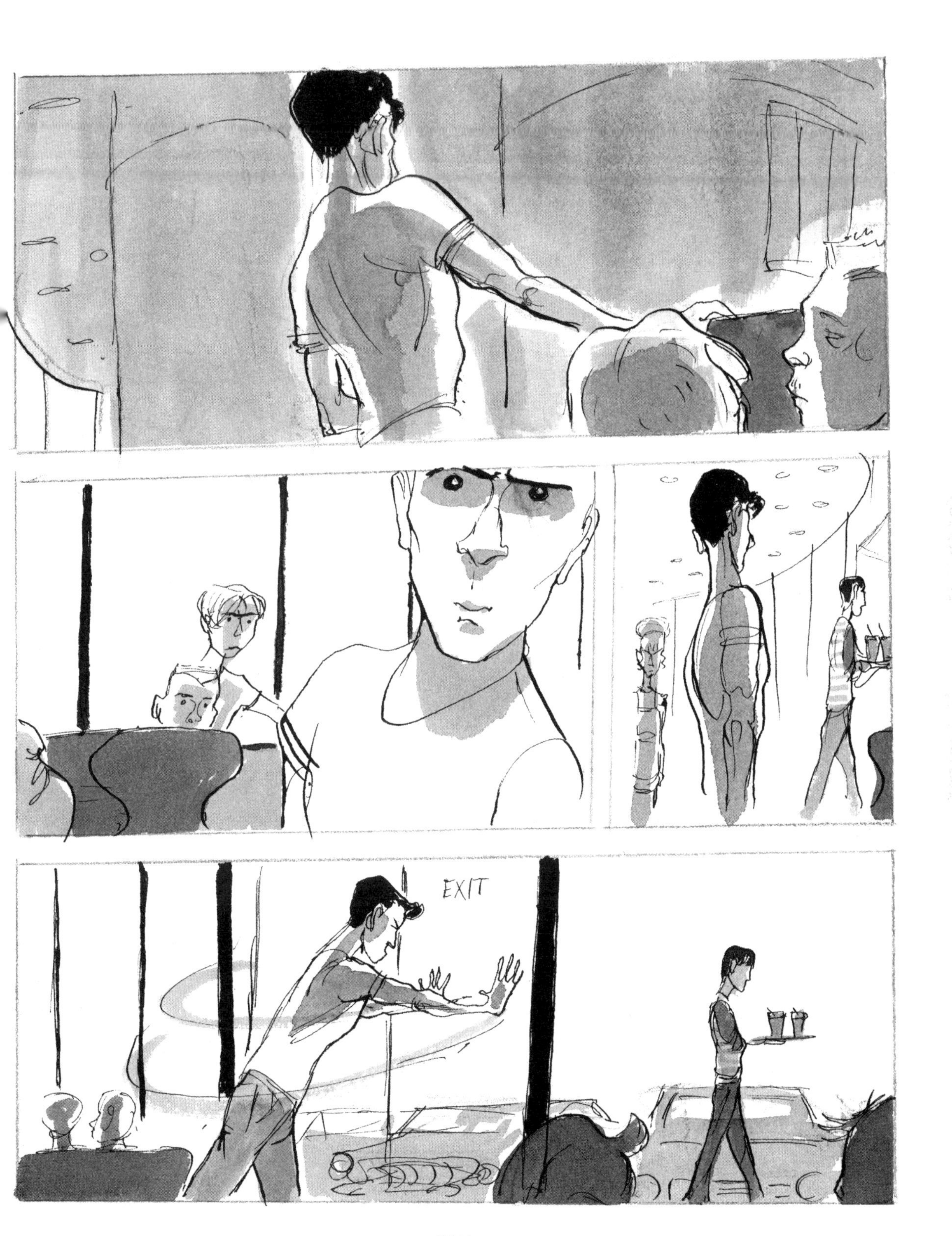
EXIT

A FIGHT!
IT'S A FIGHT!

'FUCK'S HE DOING?

STAND UP, FAGGOT!

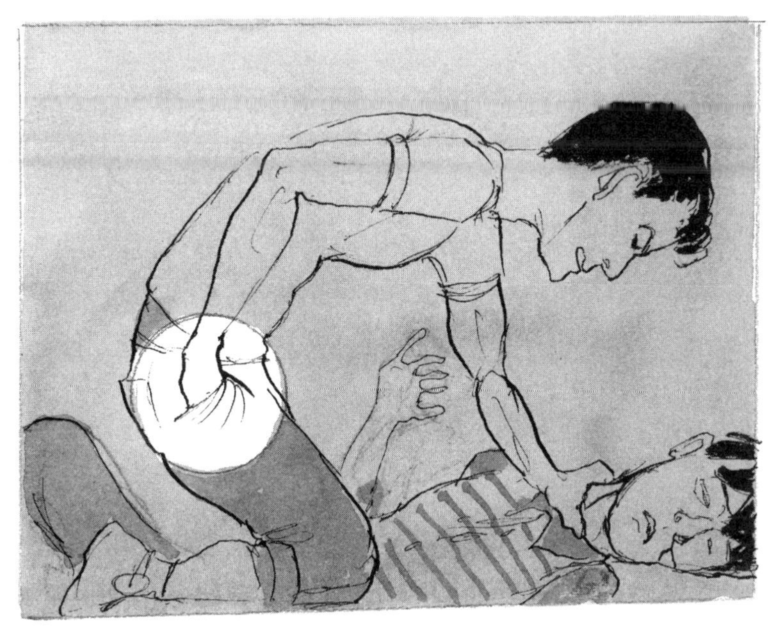

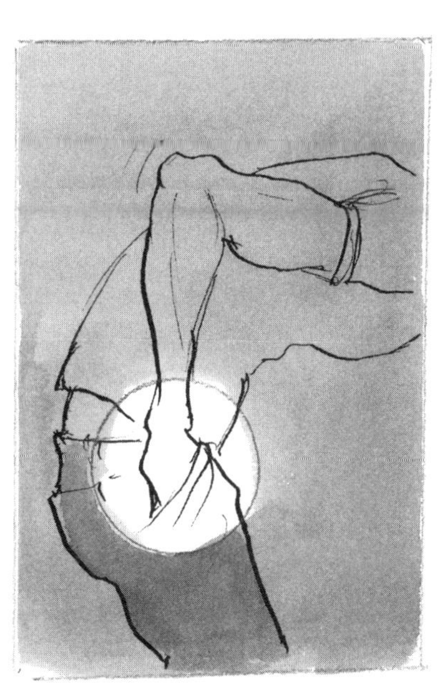

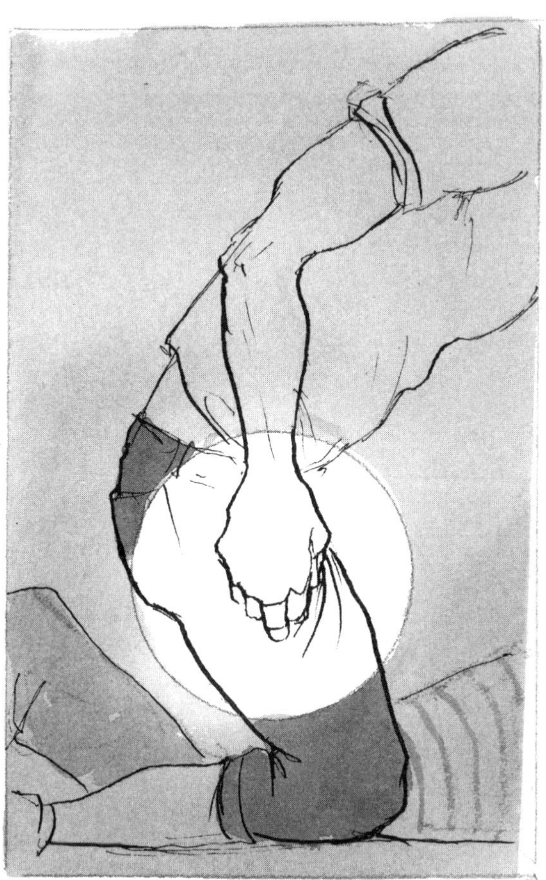

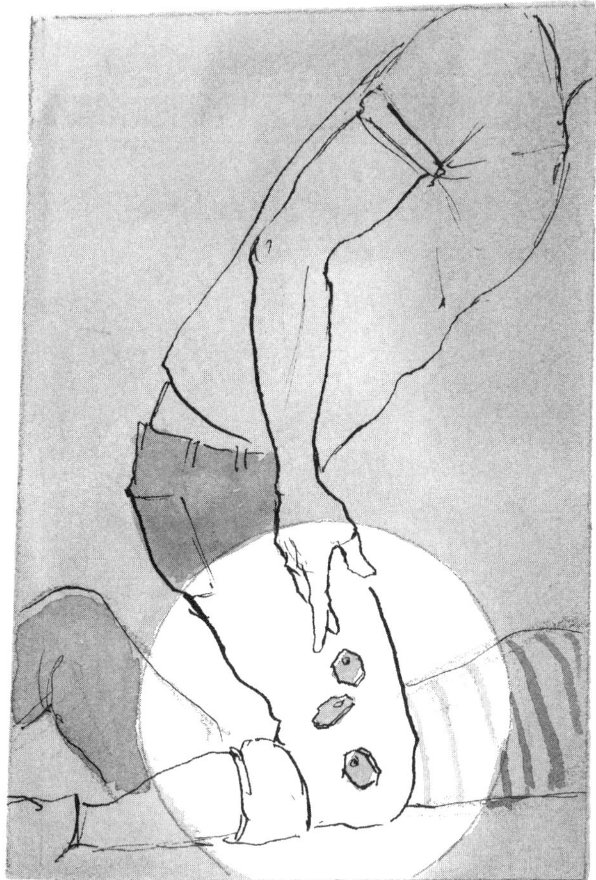

STAND UP AND FIGHT ME, YOU FUCKIN' QUEER!

WHAT'S THIS?

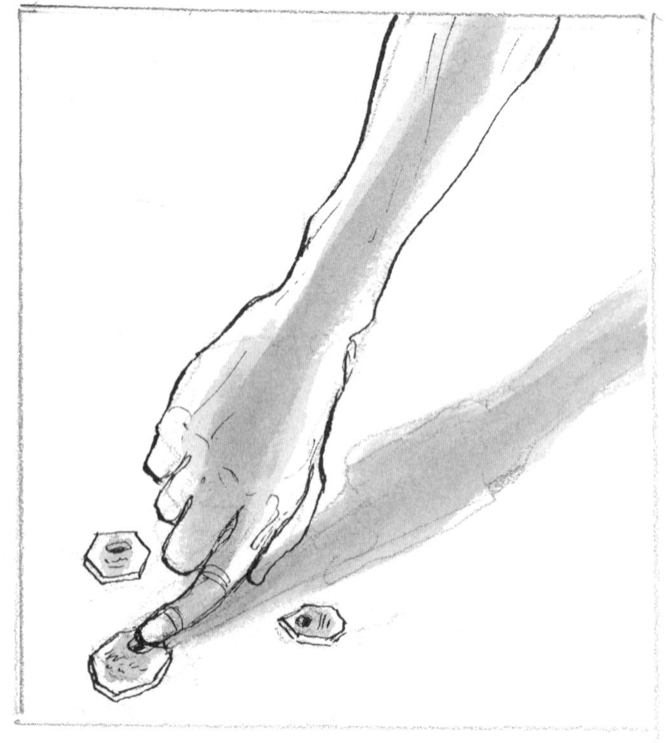

LOOK! THESE FELL OUT OF HIS POCKET!

WHAT'S GOING ON?
NOT SURE. I CAN'T SEE.

THEY'RE TAGS.
THREE DOG TAGS.

SO? THE QUEER COL-LECTS DOG TAGS?

THOSE DOGS IN THE CULVERT HAD NO TAGS!

THREE DOGS. NO TAGS!

IT'S THE "ANIMAL KILLER"!

THE FAG'S THE ANIMAL KILLER!

LOOK! WHAT THE FUCK IS THAT?

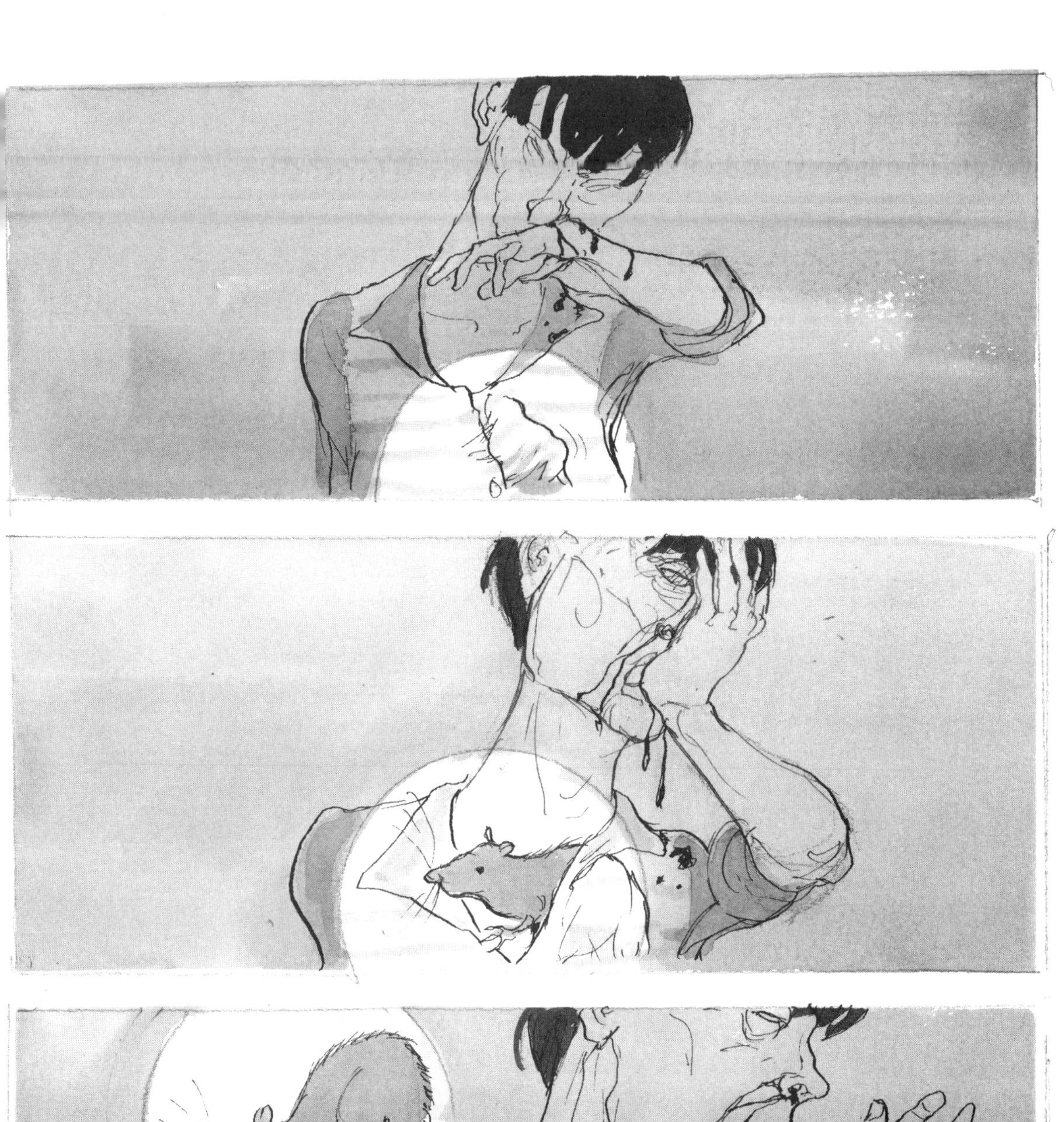

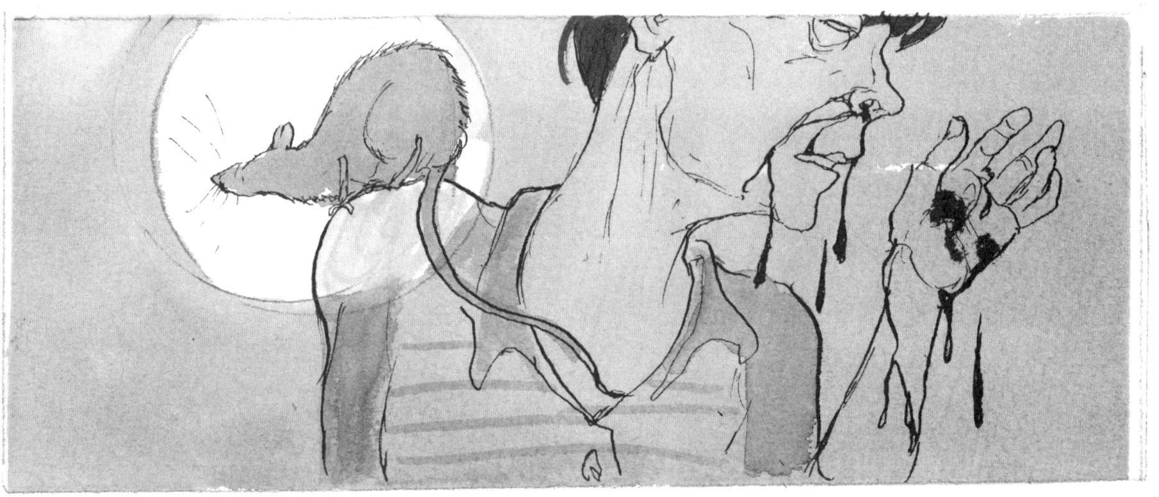

IT'S A RAT!

KILL THE QUEER!

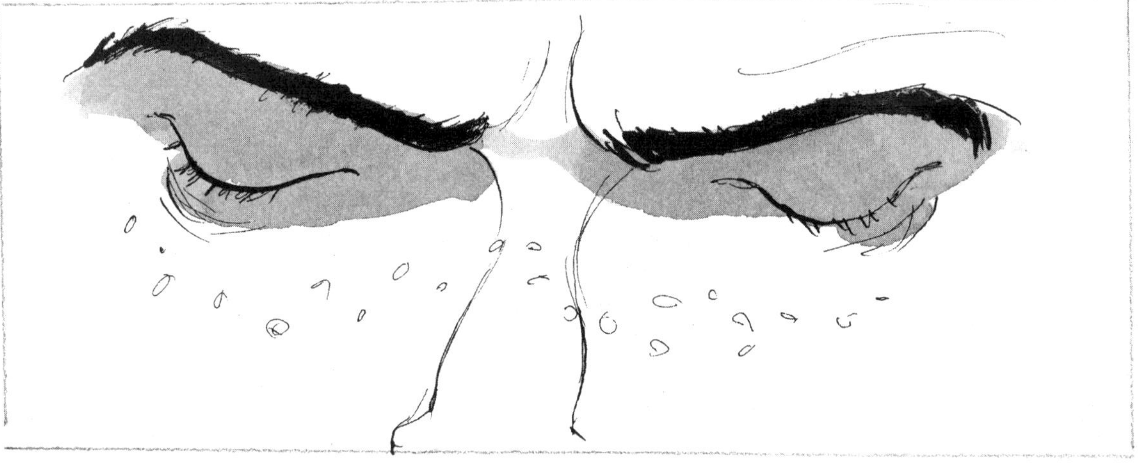

RUSS!
RUSS, WAKE UP!
WE'VE GOT TO DO SOMETHING!
RIGHT.

YOU BASTARDS!

OHHHHHH!

IN THE END IT WAS WILLIE WHO DID SOMETHING.

CHICKEN SHIT THAT I WAS, I WENT OFF WITH KURT.
WE GOT HIM!

CHAPTER FIFTEEN

FOR THREE WEEKS I BURIED MYSELF AT THE MAHS', MOWING THEIR LAWN, WASHING DISHES, TAKING OUT THE GARBAGE, TRYING TO DESERVE THEIR WELCOME. BUT IN THOSE LONG, SILENT DAYS I COULDN'T TURN OFF MY OWN THOUGHTS. AT LAST, I HAD TO FIND WARREN.

HULLO?
ANYBODY HOME?

WARREN?
IT'S RUSSELL PRUITT.
HULLO?

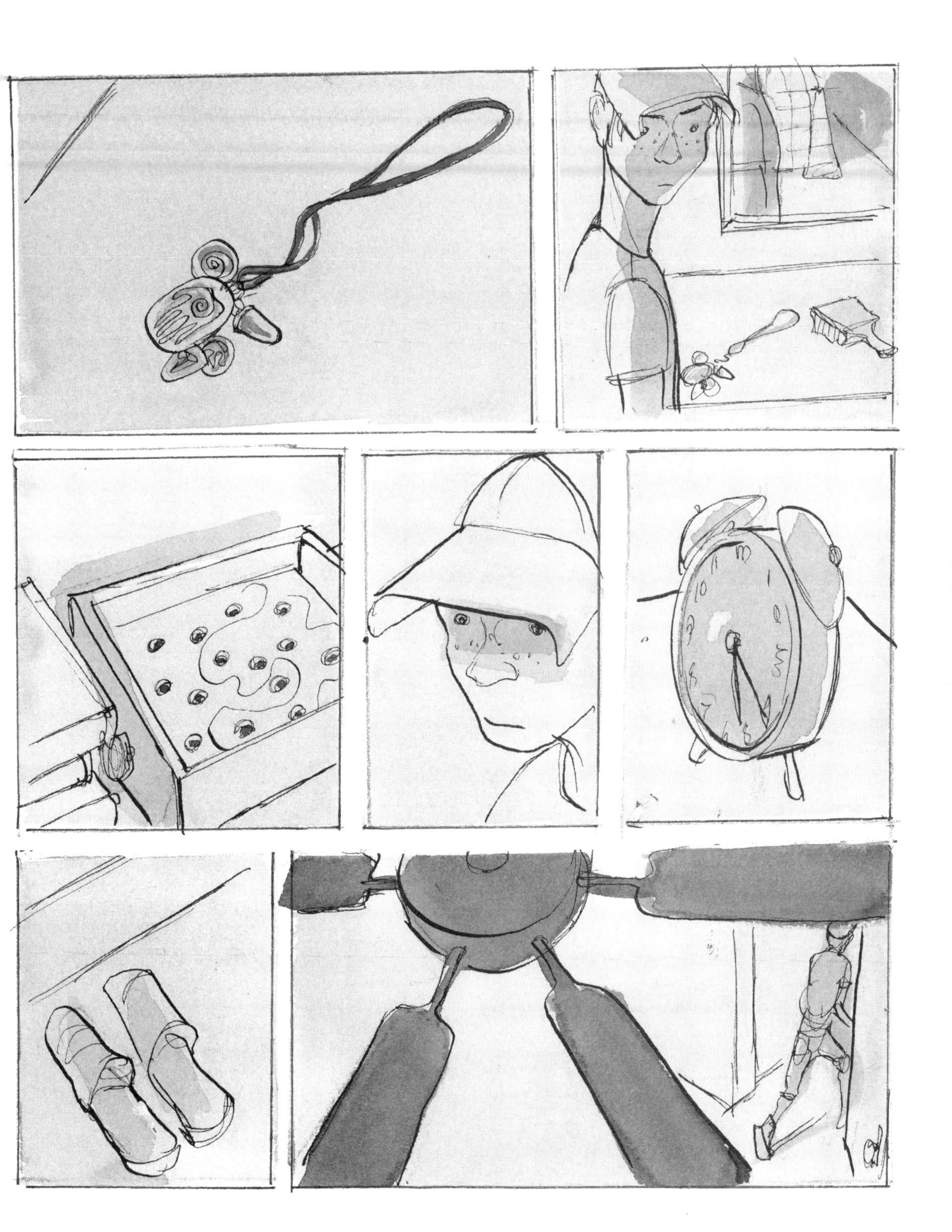

HEY, BOY!

JUST A SECOND.

DO YOU KNOW THOSE PEOPLE?

I WAS LOOKING FOR THE McCAWS?
SHE'S GONE! SHE LOADED UP HER TRUCK AND TOOK OFF, THREE DAYS AGO!
I WANTED TO HAVE A WORD WITH HER.
I WOULD HAVE AST HER IF I COULD HAVE SUMMA THESE LAWN ORNAMINS.
BUT BEFO' I COULD GET DRESSED, SHE WAS OFF! IN A CLOUD OF DUST!
DO YOU KNOW WHERE THEY WENT?
THEY? I ALREADY TOLE YOU, THE OLD LADY WENT OFF BY HERSEFF!
WHAT ABOUT WARREN?

I GUESS YOU AIN'T HEARD
THAT BOY HUNG HISSELF
FROM THAT TREE.
HE DONE IT A WEEK AGO ON SATURDAY NIGHT.

YOU CAN SEE WHERE HE KICKED THE CHAIR AWAY.

I SURE HOPE NOBODY GETS THEY HANS ON THESE LAWN ORNAMINS. THERE'S A FEW I LIKE IN PARTICULAR!
ROWF!
YIP YIP
BARK BARK BARK

Greetings

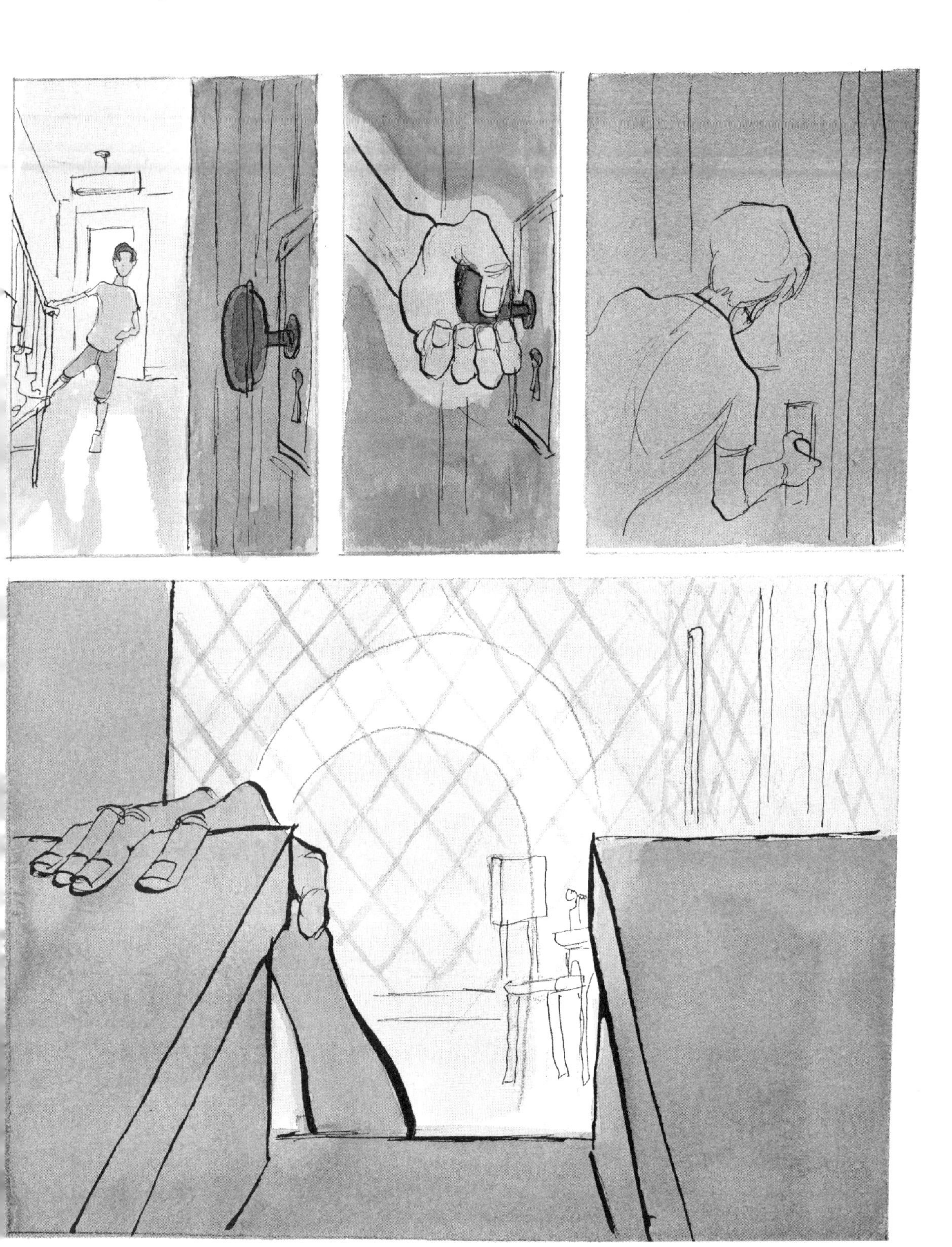

CHAPTER SIXTEEN

BAKERSFIELD WAS 500 MILES. I FIGURED I COULD DO 70 MILES A DAY AND BE THERE IN A WEEK.
CALIFORNIA

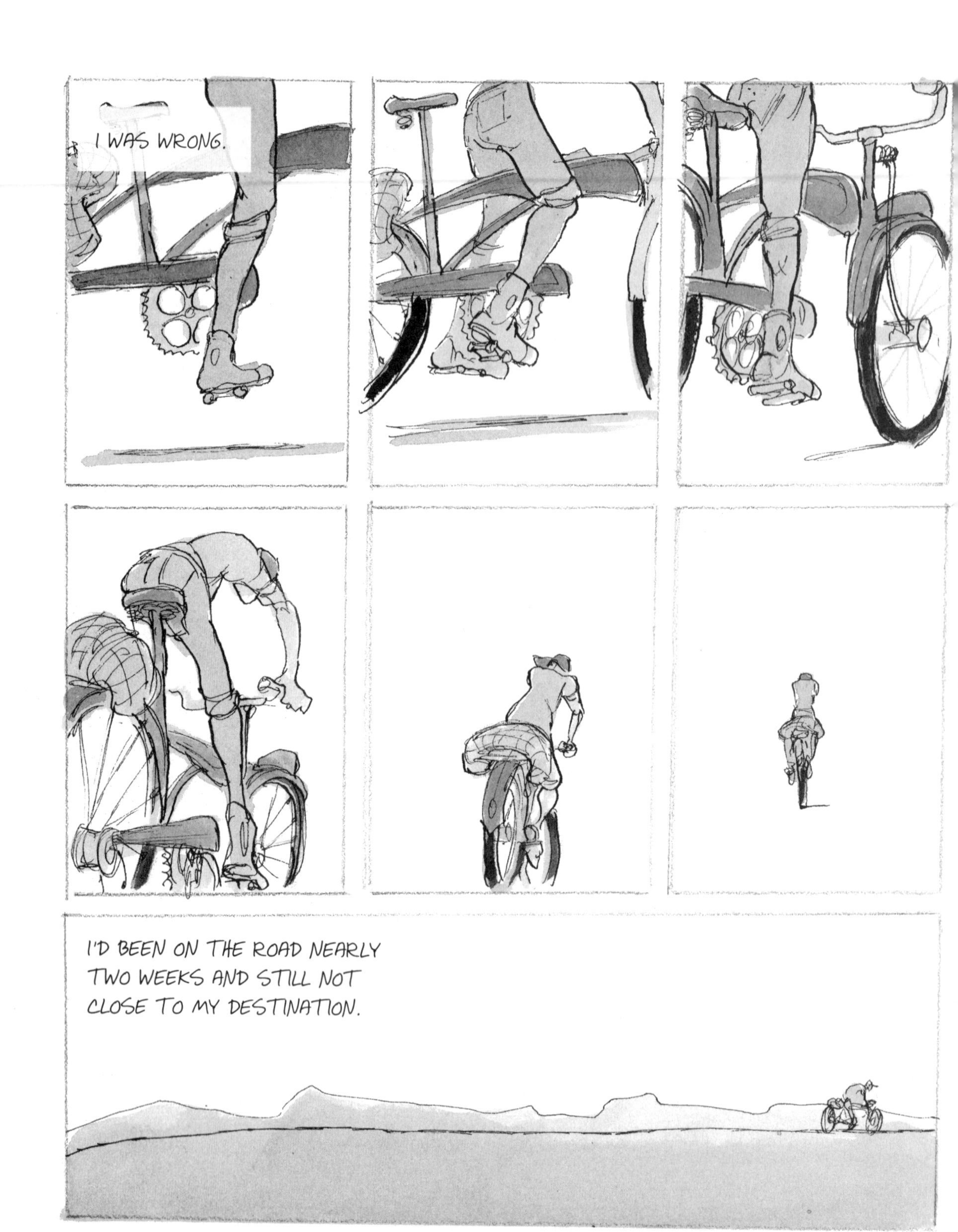
I WAS WRONG.
I'D BEEN ON THE ROAD NEARLY TWO WEEKS AND STILL NOT CLOSE TO MY DESTINATION.

I HADN'T FIGURED ON THE WEATHER. COLD AND RAIN IN MARIN . . .

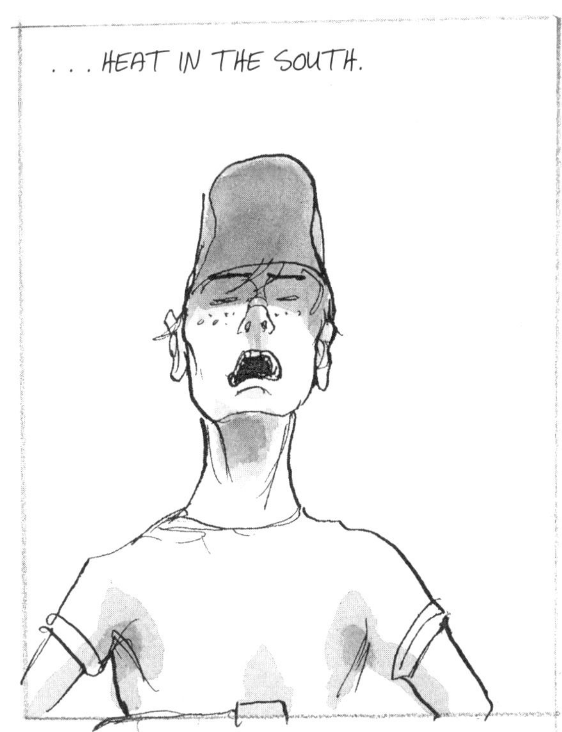
. . . HEAT IN THE SOUTH.

AT NIGHT I LOOKED FOR SAFE PLACES TO SLEEP . . .

. . . BUT MAINLY I SLEPT IN
THE ROADSIDE BRUSH, WHERE
MY BIGGEST FEARS WERE
RATTLESNAKES . . .

. . . AND TARANTULAS,
OF WHICH I'D SEEN PLENTY
ON THE ROAD.

BUT THE BIGGEST DANGERS
CAME FROM DOGS . . .

. . . AND OTHER KIDS.

I DID WITNESS SOME WONDROUS THINGS: A PACK OF COYOTES DOING THEIR APACHE DANCE IN AN OPEN FIELD AT DUSK . . .

. . . AND A STAG HIT BY A TRUCK.

IT LOOKED LIKE IT WOULD KEEP GOING UP AND UP . . .

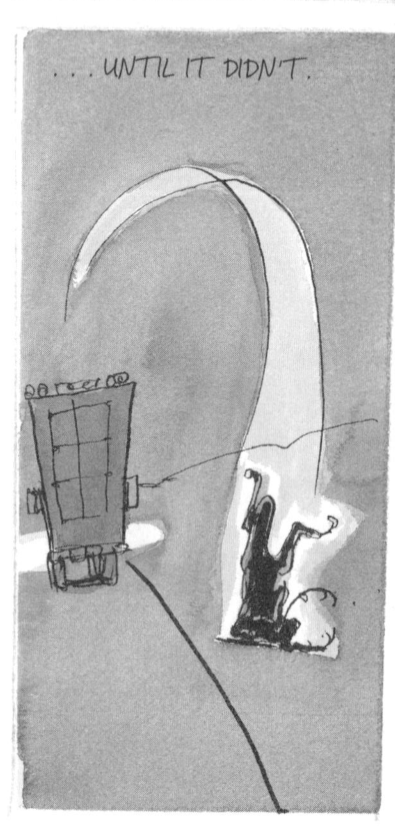
. . . UNTIL IT DIDN'T.

FINALLY, NORTH OF FRESNO, I GAVE UP.

BAKERSFIELD? YOU GOT RELATIVES THERE?

NO. I NEED TO FIND SOMEONE.

I NEED TO MAKE AN APOLOGY.

YOU RODE ALL THIS WAY TO MAKE AN APOLOGY? WHY NOT PHONE THEM UP? OR SEND A CARD!

I DON'T KNOW WHERE SHE LIVES. I'M NOT EVEN SURE OF HER NAME.
OH. WELL. THAT IS A PROBLEM.

WHERE WILL YOU STAY IN BAKERSFIELD?
DUNNO.
THAT'S ANOTHER PROBLEM.
YOU HAVE A LOT OF PROBLEMS, SON.

I HAVE ONLY ONE BIG PROBLEM.

I WANT TO LIVE WITHOUT HURTING ANYONE.

WELL, I GUESS THAT'S POSSIBLE . . .

IF YOU'RE A MOLLUSK!
HEH.

BUT I'M JUST A TIRED OLD HOUND. MY OPINION ISN'T WORTH MUCH.

YOU'VE GOT SOME MONEY, I HOPE.

YESSIR . . .
I STOLE SOME.

YOU STOLE SOME MONEY AND YOU WANT TO LIVE WITHOUT HURTING ANYONE. SON, IT SEEMS LIKE YOU'VE GOT THINGS TURNED AROUND BASS-ACKWARDS.

YESSIR. I HAVE.

IF I COULD, I'D TURN AROUND AND TAKE YOU BACK TO MARSHFIELD. BUT I GOT ME A SICK WIFE AT HOME AND I CAN'T LEAVE HER.

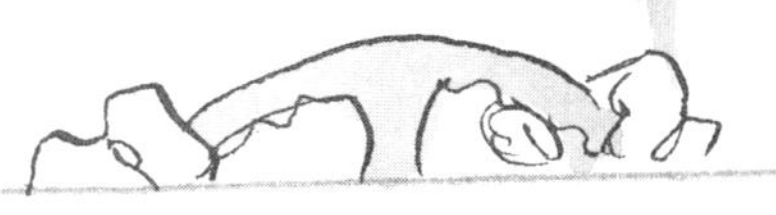

THE BUS STATION IS OVER THERE. YOU CAN WASH UP IN THEIR MEN'S ROOM. AND I MIGHT ADD, YOU COULD DO WITH A GOOD WASH!

BUS

TELEPHO

TELEPH

TELEPHO

I HAD COME WITH NO PLAN. I THOUGHT THE URGENCY OF MY QUEST WOULD, BY SOME PSYCHIC MAGNETISM, DRAW WARREN'S GRANDMA TO ME. BUT THE HECTIC ENERGY OF THE CITY BROKE MY FOCUS.

FOR THREE DAYS I WATCHED FOR THAT RUSTY OLD FORD PICKUP WITH WARREN'S GRANDMA IN IT.

FINDING PLACES TO SLEEP WAS A PROBLEM.

AND, WHEN I DID SLEEP, I HAD A RECURRING DREAM.

I WAS IN A VAST PLACE OF SHADOWS AND STAIRS. THE ONLY WAY TO GET OUT WAS TO CLIMB UP.

BUT EACH STAIRWAY I
CHOSE CLOSED IN ON ME AND
STOPPED MY PROGRESS.

POKE

WAKE UP, PUNK.

WHAT'RE YOU DOING SLEEPING IN OUR PARK?
THIS IS OUR TERRITORY, MAN.

I . . .

WHAT DID YOU SAY?

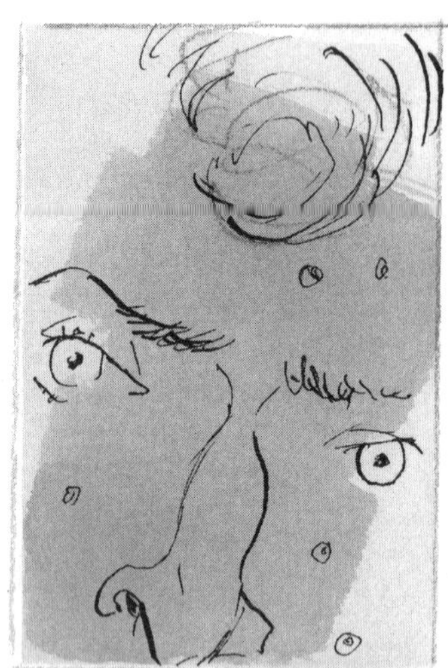

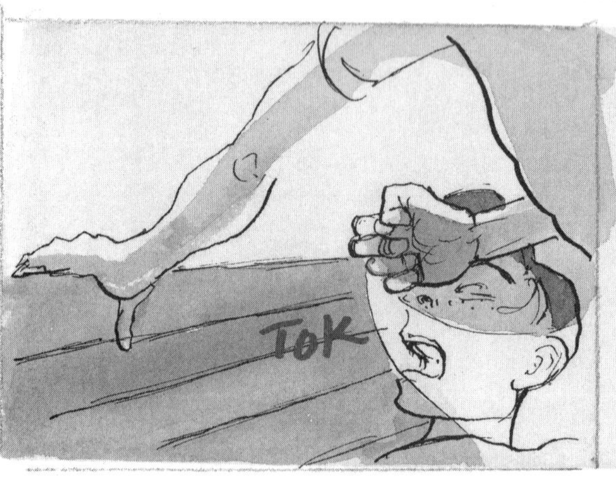
TOK

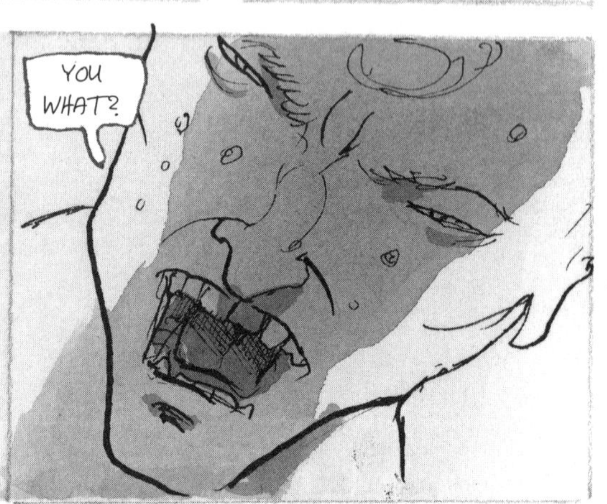
YOU WHAT?

I GOT HIS BIKE!
YEEEEEEEEEHAWWWWW!

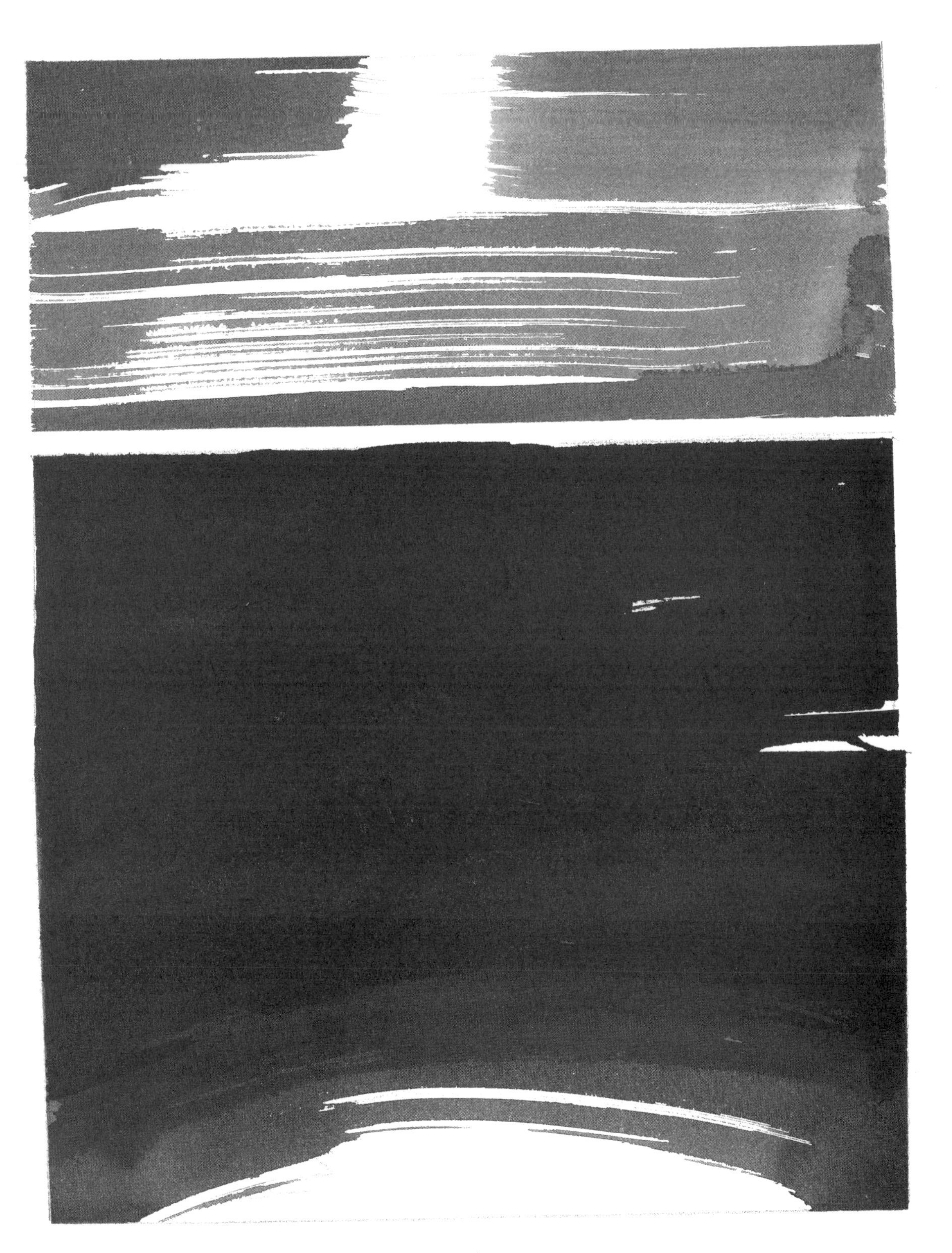

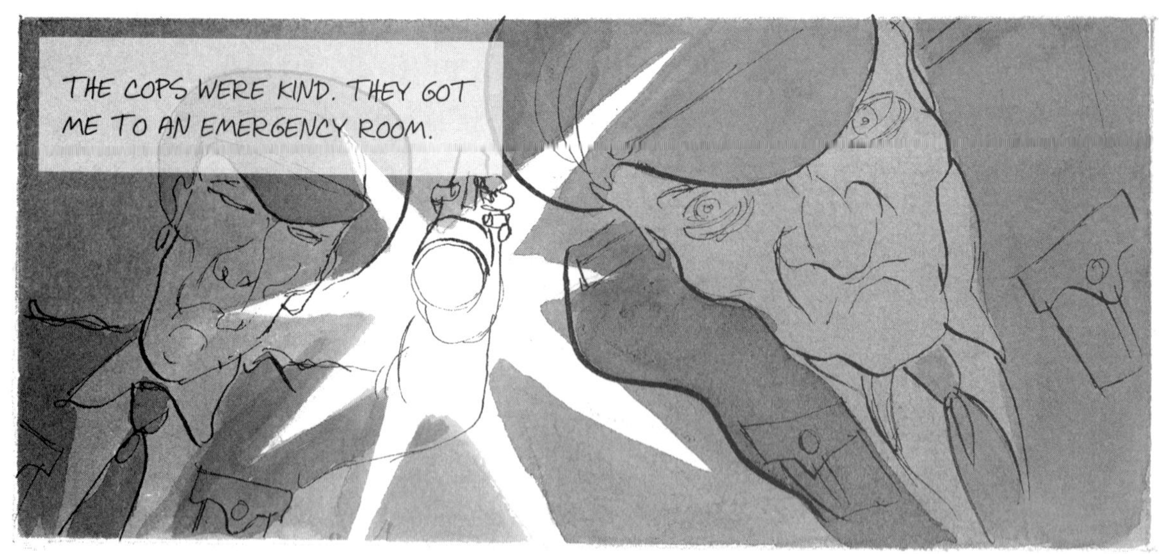
THE COPS WERE KIND. THEY GOT ME TO AN EMERGENCY ROOM.

NEXT DAY, THEY GAVE ME TWO BUCKS AND A TICKET TO SAN RAFAEL.
BUS

IS MR. MAH VERY ANGRY WITH ME?

HE IS VERY ANGRY WITH YOU. YOU STOLE FROM HIM!

HE SAID HE WILL NOT TAKE YOU BACK IN HIS HOUSE . . .

. . . BUT I TOLD HIM YOU ARE A GOOD BOY AND YOU HAVE NO PLACE TO GO!

I'LL GO BACK TO OUR OLD HOUSE.
YOU CAN'T! THE BANK TOOK IT BACK. YOUR FATHER NEVER PAID THE MORTGAGE!

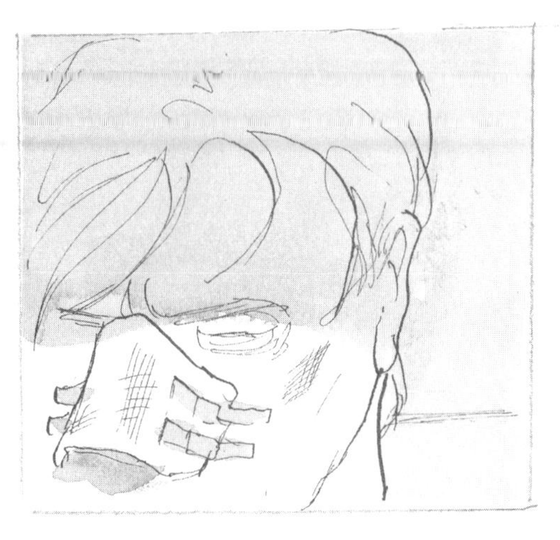

RUSSELL, YOU HAVE TO UNDERSTAND.

MR. MAH IS A VERY TRADITIONAL CHINESE MAN. HE WORRIES A LOT ABOUT MONEY. WHEN YOU STOLE FROM HIM . . .

. . . HE FELT BETRAYED. HE HAD TREATED YOU LIKE A SON.

I'M NOBODY'S SON.

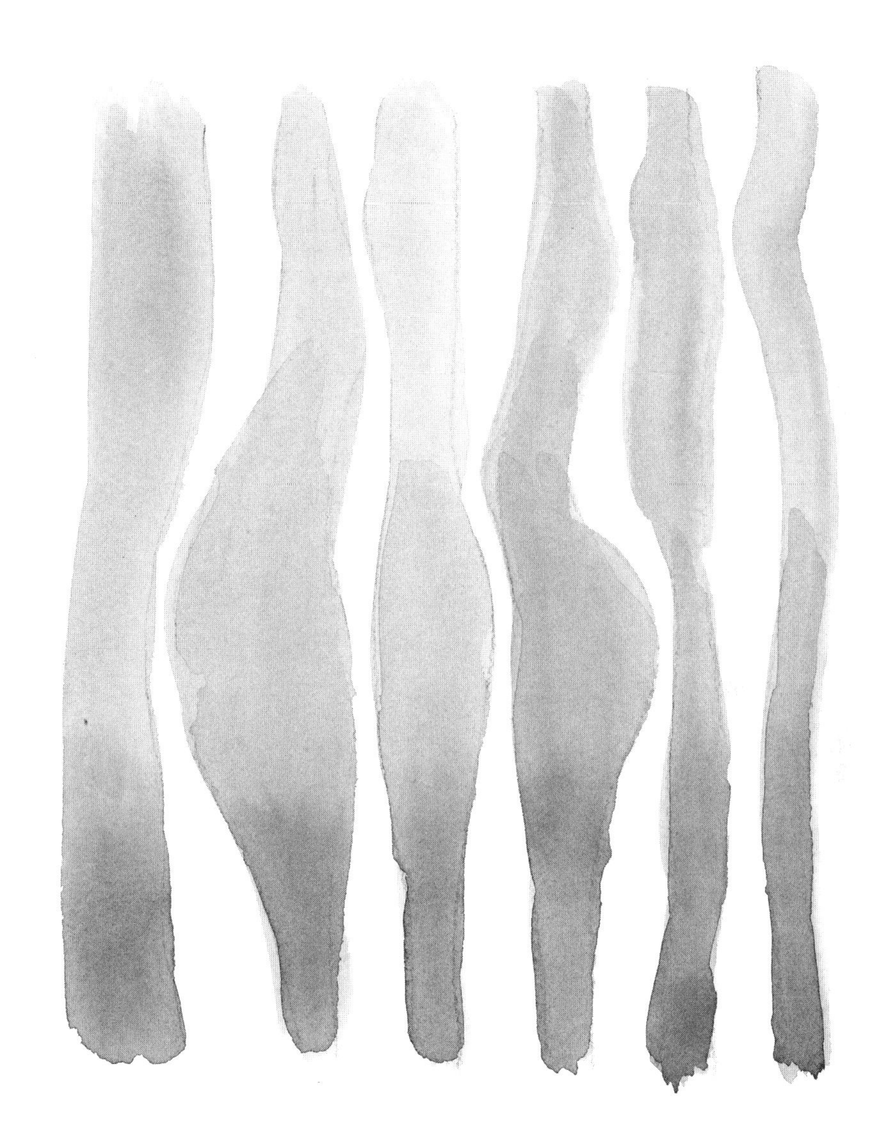

OKAY. IF I HAD TO LIVE AMONG PEOPLE I WOULD BECOME THE MOLLUSK.
I COULD WASH DISHES, PEEL SHRIMP, AND BUS TABLES WITHOUT MUCH INTERACTION AT ALL.

THE INDEPENDENT
SUSPECT ANIMAL KILLER
CAUGHT!
THE INDEPEND
SUSPECT ANIMAL KILLER
CAUGHT!
History of
Violence and
Mental Illness
THIS NEWS SHOULD, BY ALL RIGHTS, HAVE MADE ME FEEL VINDICATED AND FREED. INSTEAD IT MADE ME FEEL EVEN MORE HOLLOW.

DAYS LATER, THE POLICE VISITED KURT FOR A CONVERSATION ABOUT THOSE DOG TAGS.

I, TOO, SHOULD HAVE BEEN UP BEFORE THE JUDGE. BUT I HADN'T MADE ANY FALSE ACCUSATIONS OR CAUSED ANYONE BODILY HARM.

BECAUSE KURT WAS A JUVENILE, INSTEAD OF PRISON HE GOT SENT TO A MILITARY SCHOOL IN ANAHEIM.
CLEARLY, WITH KURT OUT OF THE PICTURE— AND EVEN BEFORE THAT—MY FRIENDSHIP WITH WILLIE HAD COME TO AN END.

DAD AND MOM . . .

KURT
AND
WILLIE . . .

AND, OF COURSE,
WARREN . . .
ALL OUT OF MY LIFE.

WHENEVER I LOOKED AT MR. MAH I SAW ACCUSATION IN HIS EYES. "YOU WORK!" THEY SAID. "YOU PAY ME BACK!"

MRS. MAH WAS ALWAYS GENTLE, BUT THE LITTLE WRINKLE OF CONCERN ON HER FOREHEAD MADE ME WANT TO SCREAM. OBVIOUSLY SHE THOUGHT I WAS A HOPELESS CASE.

MR. MAH SMILED AT ME WHEN I PAID HIM BACK HIS $65. I DON'T KNOW WHAT ELSE I EXPECTED.
FIREWORKS? A TROPHY? A PARADE?

ALASKA BECKONED SERIOUSLY NOW. I HAD NO MONEY AND NO BIKE, BUT I COULD HITCHHIKE. I WOULD CHALLENGE THE TERRORS IN ME.

RUSSELL.
RUNNING AWAY AGAIN?

I CAN'T STAY HERE.

HE'S STILL MAD AT ME AND I'M A BURDEN ON YOU.

RUSSELL, YOU ARE NOT A BURDEN, AND MR. MAH IS NOT MAD AT YOU. HE SAYS YOU ARE A VERY GOOD CARROT-CHOPPER! HE IS PLANNING TO GIVE YOU MORE RESPONSIBILITY.
HE THINKS YOU WILL MAKE A VERY GOOD SOUS-CHEF ONE DAY.

"CARROT-CHOPPER"!
WONDERFUL!

RUSSELL, I WANT YOU TO KNOW SOMETHING.

YOU AND MR. MAH ARE VERY MUCH ALIKE.

YOU FEEL ALONE? HE FEELS VERY MUCH ALONE.

YOU CANNOT GO BACK TO OHIO? HE CAN NEVER GO BACK TO CHINA. YOUR FAMILY IS LOST? HIS FAMILY ARE ALL DEAD.
MR. MAH WORKS VERY HARD, BUT THE NEIGHBORS SEE ONLY A "CHINAMAN" WHO BELONGS IN A LAUNDRY.
THEY ARE BLIND TO WHO HE REALLY IS.
HIS ONLY HOME IS IN THE FOOD HE COOKS.

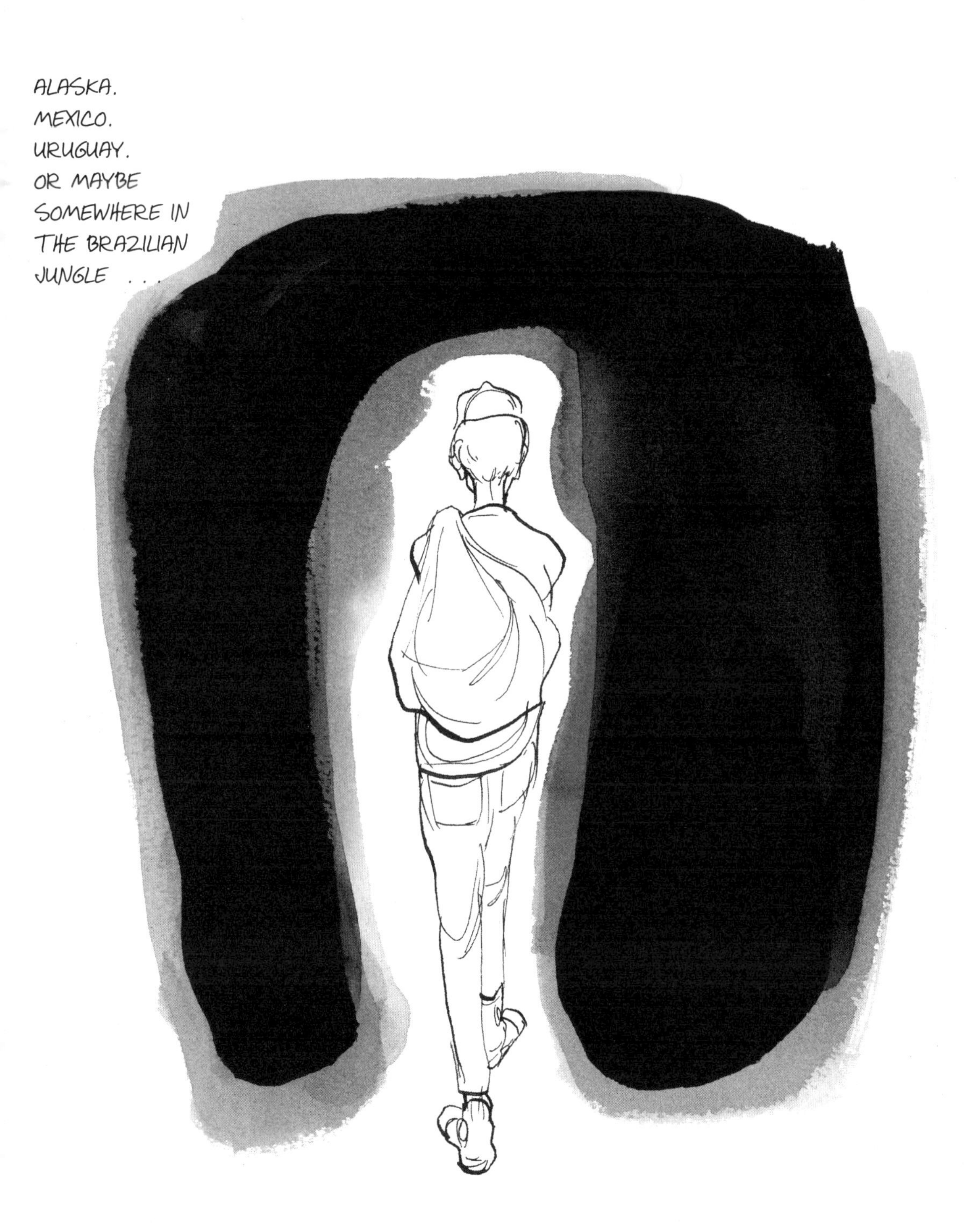
ALASKA.
MEXICO.
URUGUAY.
OR MAYBE
SOMEWHERE IN
THE BRAZILIAN
JUNGLE . . .

CHAPTER SEVENTEEN

I LIKE THE GARDEN AT NIGHT, ITS TANGLED SHAPES SIMPLIFIED.

IN THE DARK I CAN'T SEE JIAN'S FACE . . .
. . . ITS IMMIGRANT'S SADNESS . . .
. . . ONLY THE SMOOTH SWING OF HIS ARMS . . .
. . . AND HIS STRONG, SURE STEPS MOVING AWAY FROM HARM.

SUPPER IS READY!

ACKNOWLEDGMENTS

To Mike Kleimo, whose wicked-keen recollections of his youth were the catalyst for this story; to Kevin Brady, Mark Guin, and Brad Zellar—all brothers of my heart—who gave freely of their memories of adolescent chaos and middle-school brutality; to my agent, Holly McGhee, for her support and sharp editorial comments through the many different versions of this book; to my editor, Bob Weil, whose generosity, enthusiasm, and good counsel never flagged for three years, despite numerous stalls and setbacks; to Marie Pantojan, Bob's steady, discerning assistant; to Anna Oler, the best art director an artist could ever wish for; to Steve Attardo, whose amazing design skills and acute editorial sense produced a bounty of great jacket comps, so hard to choose from; to Joe Lops and Nat Kent, who did most of the behind-the-scenes heavy lifting on this project; to Peter Miller, to Nick Curley, and to my old friend Kate Kubert, who made all the publicity and marketing cogs and wheels run with seeming ease; to my *homies* Robert and Bill Trenary, who were with me on this ride from the start, who leaned with the sharpest curves and held on through the skids and near-collisions, always with forbearance and good humor; and, lastly, to Anita Chong for her penetrating and granular editorial advice, and—during one wintry week in Toronto—for lifting me up and setting me back on my creative feet when I needed it most.

ABOUT THE AUTHOR

David Small started his illustration career as an editorial artist for national publications such as *The New Yorker*, the *New York Times*, the *Washington Post*, *Esquire*, and *Playboy*. As the author and illustrator of numerous picture books for children, his books have been translated into several languages, made into animated films and musicals, and have won many of the top awards accorded to illustration, including the 2001 Caldecott Medal, two Caldecott Honor Awards, the Society for Illustrators' Gold Medal, and, twice, the Christopher Medal. In 2009 Small's illustration career took a dramatic turn with the publication of his graphic memoir, *Stitches*, which became a *New York Times* bestseller, a National Book Award Finalist, and received the American Library Association's Alex Award. To date, *Stitches* has been translated into ten foreign languages.

Small and his wife, the writer Sarah Stewart, make their home in an 1833 manor house on a bend of the St. Joseph River in Michigan.